Praise

Engaging and beautifully w... resource for anyone who wants to promote health and resilience in children. Absolutely on my must-read list for parents, caregivers, clinicians, faculty, and students.

Lisa Pearl, MS, RD, CEDS-S
Founder, CNC360
Educator, Clinical Consultant, and Supervisor

As a therapist and, most importantly, a mom of two young boys, I am deeply moved by Heidi's latest work, Nurture. She provides a relatable, non-judgmental narrative to influence our parenting when it comes to introducing food choices and laying a healthy foundation of body acceptance for our littles. I will certainly offer Nurture as a resource to my clients, as many are navigating their own parenting journeys while breaking generational cycles regarding their own bodies and nutrition.

Sara Hart, MA, LMHC
Psychotherapist and Eating Disorders Expert

This is the book we have all been waiting to read. Heidi's natural and authentic voice shines through and helps the reader feel safe. You feel like you are sitting in her living room and chatting with an expert on food and body image. It is filled with heartfelt commentary on how to help maneuver hard situations with loved ones. It is truly a book for everyone.

Beth Mayer, LICSW
Eating Disorders Expert and Clinical Consultant
Former Executive Director of The Multi-Service Eating Disorders
Association (MEDA)

In this second installment from Heidi Schauster, we hear the wise and thoughtful voice of a dietitian, a somatic therapist, a writer, and a mother. Heidi speaks clearly from her experience. As a mother and therapist myself, I find her words comforting and validating.

Figuring out our roles with growing children, especially if we have faced our own trauma, disordered eating, or other challenges—as we all have—is not easy. Heidi keeps it simple around how we must attend to our own experience so we can best attend to our kids'. She writes, "Embodiment is the experience of being at home in our bodies." At the end of the day, this is the key to living our fullest lives. I will have multiple copies of Nurture *(as well as* Nourish*) to hand to anxious, loving parents as a balm to soothe their worried minds. Thank you, Heidi, for another 10/10!*

Lauren Manasse, LICSW, CEDS-S
Certified Eating Disorders Specialist and Supervisor

Nurture *is a much-needed resource for childhood-feeding questions and concerns. It offers guidance on how and why it is of utmost importance to raise our next generation in a way that promotes body acceptance and food neutrality. Heidi's voice is both reassuring and directive with evidence-based strategies to support all families in their paths toward health.*

Amy Cantor, MPH, RD
Dietitian and Eating Disorders Expert

I wholeheartedly endorse Nurture. *This book offers an inspirational approach for parents to talk to their kids about food, hunger, and body image. It does not have to be so hard. In the United States, the self-care industry is booming; there is pressure to perfectly take care of ourselves each day by eating well, meditating, exercising. The reality is, even with our best efforts, we have bad days and get off track. The diet industry endorses rigid ways of thinking that no one can ever sustain. Heidi promotes moderation and letting kids discover their own individual hungers. The wonderful news for parents is that feeding their children can be relatively easygoing. It is an important book for our time, and I believe every parent*

Praise for *Nurture*

could benefit from reading it. Many of the approaches suggested carry over to other parts of life. Thank you, Heidi, for this timely contribution to the literature of parenting.

Hannah Saxe, LICSW
Psychotherapist, Consultant, and Eating Disorders Expert

Nurture beautifully describes how our approach to feeding children is a source of body care, confidence, and connection. A must-read for caregivers looking for a "whole person" approach to feeding children.

Sarah McAllister, MS, RD, LDN
Nutrition Therapist and Eating Disorders Expert

nurture

how to raise kids who love food, their bodies, and themselves

Jason ~
May you always
nurture yourself &
those you love with
care!
♡ Heidi

HEIDI SCHAUSTER, MS, RD, CEDS-S, SEP

For information about this title or to order other books
and/or electronic media, contact the author directly:
Heidi Schauster, MS, RD, CEDS-S, SEP
Nourishing Words Nutrition Therapy and Somatic Experiencing™
617-877-2202
http://anourishingword.com
heidi@anourishingword.com

ISBNs:
978-0-9995120-2-9 (paperback)
978-0-9995120-3-6 (eBook)
978-0-9995120-4-3 (audiobook)

Library of Congress Control Number: 2023921607
Printed in the United States of America
Cover and Interior design: 1106 Design

For Ava and Kyla

The sun, the moon, and all my stars . . .

Table of Contents

Introduction
Prevention and Compassion for Parents

I believe that most of us have the capacity to have an easeful, nourishing relationship with food, body, and self. That said, getting there in this culture, with its confusing messages about eating and bodies, is not a smooth road for many. Over the last nearly thirty years in practice as a nutrition and body-image therapist, I have witnessed countless teens and adults who feel confused about food, hateful toward their bodies, and unclear about themselves.

Then, many of them transform before my eyes, after doing the hard work of finding ways to practice coming back to themselves. While disordered eating and body dissatisfaction halt growth—physical and psychological—the recovery from these challenges often brings out the most authentic and strongest parts of the people who embark on the healing work. My aim is to share what I have learned in this collaborative work toward peaceful eating and true embodiment in order to support you, your families, and the young people in your care.

This book is not just for families that have been plagued by eating disorders or challenges around body shame and dissatisfaction. It's also for those who want to keep these from occurring in the young people they care about. I have some clear ideas about how we can change the discussion around food and bodies in our families and broader communities for the better.

Still, this book alone will not prevent the children you love from developing unhealthy relationships with food or their bodies. It may not prevent them from developing eating disorders, the deadliest of all psychiatric disorders. Many forces in our world encourage disordered eating and problems relating to the self and body. While not all disordered or dysregulated eating patterns are life-threatening, most are life-altering and life-robbing. The effects of starvation, yo-yo dieting, and binge eating can be significant.

I wish I had a foolproof recipe for preventing these devastating states of mind and body in children and teens—and eventually in grown-ups. Problematic eating and body image in young people often last far into adulthood when left untreated. After nearly three decades treating kids, teens, adults, and families—and as a parent myself, raising two now-young-adult daughters—I have some thoughts about creating an atmosphere where kids grow up to love food, their bodies, and themselves. I certainly don't have all the answers, but I'd like to share what I've learned.

I'm doing this because I hear over and over from parents that they want help in this area. There are so many conflicting

Introduction

ideas and messages bouncing around about how to eat, feed, and raise children well. I sincerely hope this book helps you take a curious look at your family and the broader culture's attitudes around food, bodies, health, and wellness. I aim to assist you in making choices that support your children's views of themselves as whole people and help them develop vital minds and bodies. You might combine this book with other resources in your community. It should not be used as a substitute for nutritional or psychological treatment (for you or a child in your care). But it might be a great place to start.

As parents, we have about twenty years or so of influence. Depending on our circumstances, we may have more or less. It's a small part of most lives. Still, it's a critical time for developing habits, values, and orientation to others and the broader world. I hope to help you sift through the confusing information available about food and health, while remembering the most important parts of caring for and feeding children. I hope this book will read like a conversation with a compassionate, knowing fellow parent who happens to have done a ton of field research on this topic. As parents, we feed our kids until they become adults who essentially make all their own choices about care and feeding. Where, oh where, is the care and feeding manual? This book is my attempt to provide one.

I have strong biases, and I'll share them. I initially worked at a large children's hospital in Boston, Massachusetts, and have been in private practice for the last couple of decades. I have seen hundreds of teens, families, and adults struggle with the consequences of disordered eating and shaky relationships with their bodies. As I mentioned earlier, the healing process often produces excellent insight and personal growth. We have to have a relationship with food; we can't just abstain from eating while we find other ways to cope with life. I have learned much about what it means to fully recover from disordered eating from my clients.

I also have lived experience, as a recovered person who had an eating disorder in my teens and into my early twenties. Now, in my fifties, I have distance from that eating disorder. I'm grateful for this perspective and all I've learned as a human being and a clinician. I don't use food (restriction or binge eating) to deal with life's challenges. However, I still have challenges, like any human. I still have the same nervous system I was born with, but now, I manage it differently.

I own my privilege as a white, middle-class, heterosexual, cisgender, small-bodied woman. I do not have lived experience navigating this culture in a large body, nor do I have intimate experience of the oppression of weight stigma many of my clients tell me about. I don't know what it feels like to not fit into restaurant seats, to not be able to find clothes that fit in a store, or to be discriminated against because of my body size, skin color, economic status, sexuality, or gender expression. I hear about this discrimination all the time, particularly stories of weight stigma, but my feelings after hearing these stories are nothing compared to what my clients in larger and more marginalized bodies experience on a regular basis.

In 2018, I published a book entitled *Nourish: How to Heal Your Relationship with Food, Body, and Self*, written for adults (or older teens). This book received three independent book awards, but the stories of countless readers are what touch me more deeply. I am grateful to those who took the time to reach out and tell me how the book has changed their lives. Many said they wish they'd had more information about developing a balanced relationship with food and body at a younger age. Many asked that I write a version of *Nourish* for parents to guide them around talking with their children about food, nutrition, dieting, health, and bodies.

While families are not to blame for eating disorders, we know there is a genetic component and that eating disorders and disordered eating patterns run in families. Well-meaning loved ones can say things that trigger feelings of shame, encouraging body discomfort and dysregulated eating. They can also model confusing food patterns and health practices to children. The family also often plays a significant part in successfully healing an eating disorder. I'm grateful to my own family for their assistance in my recovery journey long ago.

Many families I've worked with experience shame that keeps them from getting the help and support they deserve. I designed this book to assist families in the challenging work of supporting their children and teens. Parents can use these influential years to steer their children toward body acceptance, balance, and habits that support connection and care of the body. That said, there are myriad forces pushing our children and teens in the opposite direction. Struggles with eating in young people are often a very real expression of pain, insecurity, and anxiety.

I grew up in the 1970s and '80s—without the internet—and developed an eating disorder. I see the pressures on young people today around image when cameras are in everyone's pockets. The way to say hello to each other is to "snap" a photo of oneself. Visual impressions mean even more in today's world. That alone is a lot to navigate when developing your sense of self as a young adult. It's tough to have a body in this world, particularly one that does not conform to the ideal standard. And it's also tough to have a body that is so "on display" and vulnerable to different kinds of trauma.

So how do we attempt to raise embodied, balanced children who become embodied, balanced adults who are comfortable in their skin and have plenty of energy for truly meaningful life pursuits? I don't have all the answers, but I hope you will feel supported and curious about my thoughts. I hope you will bring your questions to fellow parents and discuss these issues in your communities. We change our culture and the forces around our children by staying conscious and taking our role as parents seriously—not in a helicopter way, but in a way that supports and values our children as individuals and as parts of a greater collective.

I feel so much compassion for all parents trying to navigate the world today. I aim to reflect that compassion and solidarity in my words in this book. Please let me know how I'm doing on this. The last thing I want to be is a know-it-all kind of parent. Life is too short for us parents not to acknowledge both our victories and struggles as we seek to find the best way to love and care for our kids.

My twin daughters, Ava and Kyla, are now dancing through their young adulthood. I've done my best in parenting them thus far, and I've definitely made mistakes along the way. I've stumbled through parenting like any other. I've learned that the stumbling is actually part of it all. I start most chapters of this book with my daughters' wisdom in quotations (with permission), because we've had many talks about food, bodies, and growing up in this culture. I think their insights are wise, located near that time of life when the sense of self develops. They have had their bodies change, felt shame, and had them on display by social media much more recently than I have. I hope you find their wisdom as inspiring as I did (I'm biased) and appreciate the vulnerability they displayed in sharing their words.

I'm sure it wasn't easy to grow up with a mom constantly asking them to listen to their bodies or pointing out subtle forms of fatphobia and body oppression everywhere. I'm confident that, even if I did overdo it at times, they got some armor against developing a complicated relationship with food. Because of my own eating-disorder history, I have had a particular interest in doing whatever I can to prevent disordered eating in my daughters, knowing full well that many factors that I have no control over encourage disordered eating and negative body image. Some of those factors are genetics, our diet- and weight-obsessed culture, mental-health challenges, traumatic events, social-media influence, and peer influence, among others.

In addition, I have told many stories throughout this book about the struggles and victories of my clients. I've changed the names and identifying information to protect their privacy. I also use the pronoun "she" a fair amount and sprinkle in a "he" and "they" here and there to mirror the demographics of my practice. I am aware that gender is not a binary construct, and my aim is not to exclude you if you do not see pronouns that you use to identify yourself. I often use "she" and "he" for ease of reading, and I apologize in advance for any challenge that my choice of wording brings up for you. Challenges with food, body, and self know no boundaries and affect all of us.

I don't mean the following ten chapters or steps to be linear, just like the ten steps in my first book, *Nourish*. I've put the steps in a particular order because it's a progression that made sense to me and which seems to play out in my work with families and clients. They are meant to be fluid, liquid steps—not fixed or rigid. They are concepts that kept coming up in my work with families and my journey as a parent.

I hope these steps will help guide you on your parenting journey and encourage balance and whole-self wellness in your family. I desire that all people, young and old, learn to identify their deepest needs, wants, and hungers and to feed themselves in such a way that they feel nurtured, loved, freed up, and ready to take on the world. Your family does not have to spend so much time agonizing about what to eat or not to eat.

Again, this book is not a substitute for the incredible healing power of therapeutic relationships and professional help. Eating disorders in your children require a team approach: psychotherapy, nutrition therapy, medical monitoring, etc. I encourage you to share concerns with trusted care providers and bring this reading into any personal health and wellness work you are already doing. Even subclinical challenges with food and body image resolve more readily with the support of professionals trained to work with disordered eating.

Lastly, please read this book with a grain of sea salt. As with any advice from a health professional—or other assorted wisdom-imparting human beings—I invite you to take the information and recommendations that resonate for you as a parent and leave the rest. You are in charge of your own journey and your journey as a parent. If the chapters bring up concerns about your relationship with food and body, consider checking out my first book, Nourish, to assist you in your healing, or seek professional help. Your own personal work may be an essential strategy for raising children who eat and regard themselves well. That said, no one knows more about what you need than you do. Trust your wisdom and intuition as an individual and as a parent. I hope this book helps you get in touch with how to nourish yourself and your family on many levels.

Ditch Dieting—for
Your Children and for You

"Eat what you like. Don't eat anything you
don't like. Eat one weird fruit per week."

~ Kyla's advice (age 17)

There are so many confusing messages about food and how
to eat. Every week there is a new "healthy-eating plan"
that is "cleaner" than the rest. They sound like well-being
breakthroughs, but many of them contradict each other. They
are diets in disguise. Many of these wellness-focused messages
are dangerous to our children's health and well-being because
they take kids away from their natural, intuitive sense about
balanced eating. In fact, research has shown that, if left to their
own devices, kids inherently eat a well-balanced, healthful diet
over the course of a week. You'll hear more about my daughter's
"weird fruit vlog" from the quote above later in the book.

In the United States alone, the diet industry is a roughly $60 billion industry. It's a thriving business based on the fact that, most of the time, the diet doesn't work. If the diet or food plan is not sustainable, we look for the next book, product, or program. We may even revisit those diets that worked in the short term, hoping that the weight loss sticks—this time. Research shows that 96% of people who go on a diet will gain any weight lost back, often plus more, because the metabolism has been lowered by the restrictive eating pattern. This can lead to a lifetime of struggle with one's body. A University of California study determined that one of the best predictors of weight gain is having been on a diet in the past year. (See references at the end of this chapter.)

Research has also shown the most significant factor for struggling with one's weight as an adult is dieting in childhood and adolescence. The results of one 2018 study showed that experiencing parental encouragement to diet as an adolescent was significantly associated with a higher risk of binge eating, engaging in unhealthy weight-control behaviors, lower body satisfaction, and "overweight/obesity" fifteen years later (as defined by the BMI, a highly flawed measurement, which I'll discuss later, but one used in most research and clinical practice). These results remain robust after adjusting for socio-demographics and baseline measures of those outcomes. Encouraging a teen to diet may encourage significant behavioral and emotional challenges around food and body as an adult. I hear about this from hundreds of my adult clients who look back and remember the first time they were put on a "well-meaning" diet.

According to the National Eating Disorder Association, 20 million women and 10 million men in the United States have had an eating disorder. This figure is likely an underestimation, as many do not come forward and report disordered eating. Persons with eating disorders have a false sense of themselves, both in the physical body and in a cohesive personal identity. Mental and physical health is affected when children and adults have a complicated relationship with food. Due to this physical-body component, eating disorders are harmful—and can be deadly.

Anorexia nervosa (the eating disorder with starvation as a hallmark) has been described as the most lethal psychiatric disorder, carrying a sixfold increased risk of death, four times the risk of major depression. (The research behind these fig- ures is about ten years old, as studies of eating disorders are meager compared to many other disorders with better-funded research.) The cost of any type of eating disorder is also high in terms of relationships drained, productive hours lost, and dreams canceled. These are the costs that we can't measure so easily in research but that I see so much evidence of in my clinical practice.

According to researcher Catherine Cook-Cottone, eating disorders are, in their most basic form, a collection of embod- ied, physical acts that develop to help people manage what they perceive as overwhelming internal and external stresses and demands. The symptoms are intentional, physical, and embodied in a way that is distinct from those of people with mood disorders, anxiety disorders, and many other mental illnesses, despite some overlap and similarities. The person with an eating disorder attempts to function by using physical behaviors designed to control the body's size, shape, and/or experience by way of a pathological involvement with food (for example, binge eating and restriction), exercise, and sometimes pharmaceuticals.

So, how do we raise children to have a healthy relationship with food and their bodies? How do we prevent suffering from eating disorders of all types: restrictive anorexia nervosa, binge-eating disorder, and all the variants in between? In the next chapter, Step 2, I'll discuss **orthorexia**, a term first introduced by Dr. Steven Bratman in 1996 for a condition in which individuals are obsessed with healthy or "clean" eating, even if they aren't obsessed with weight. Healthful eating is not really health-promoting when it becomes an overwhelming, obsessive behavior that creates conflicts within the self.

One of my first recommendations to parents or caregivers who want to raise kids to be wise about food, body, and self is to, ideally, be someone who is not on a diet or restricting food unless medically necessary. If you are, try to keep it out of your child's consciousness as much as possible. (Know that this is nearly impossible once they get to about age seven.) Restrictive eating is not sustainable for most humans. It creates foods that are "charged" or "bad" and more attractive than they need to be. If you want your child to develop health-giving, balanced eating habits, you will ideally practice moderate eating yourself. If you are a chaotic eater who goes back and forth between restricting and eating frenetically or compulsively, your children will likely imitate this as they learn how to regulate their own eating and appetites.

Step 1

Trust me, they are watching.

I have supported people with disordered eating for the past thirty years. Many adult clients I work with who struggle with compulsive eating have either imitated dieting parents or were put on a diet at a young age by a well-meaning caregiver or medical professional. As I mentioned, several studies have shown that dieting in childhood and adolescence is the most significant risk factor for struggling with one's weight as an adult. I have heard many clients in my nutrition-therapy practice describe parents caught up in the vicious cycle of restricting and yo-yo weight gain. This made it genuinely confusing for them to learn how to eat in a balanced, sustainable way based on their bodies' cues versus the food plan of the day.

If you are starting to worry about your own eating habits and the influence that they might have on the children around you, you are not alone. Sadly, research indicates that four out of five American women are dissatisfied with how they look, with half on a restrictive diet. One study by Kimberly Hempworth in 2010 determined that 80% of ten-year-old girls had dieted in their short life. This statistic is frankly shocking, and I hope that things are shifting as our awareness of eating problems increases. Going on a restrictive diet is a predictor of increased body weight, particularly if you went on a diet during your childhood or teen years. The risk of disordered eating and a long-term struggle with your body, however, is more concerning. Instead of developing self-esteem based on your unique strengths, dieting encourages an unhealthy pre-occupation with the body and its shape during the formative growing years.

I tell my nutrition-therapy clients that I don't do weight-loss counseling because I feel it's unethical. There is no evidence-based food plan that leads to sustainable weight loss. Absolutely none. **Furthermore, focusing on weight would reduce the person in front of me to a body and miss what I firmly believe are the true determinants of health and well-being:**

- **social support**

- **economic support**

- **access to good preventative and acute health care**

- **management of life stress**

- **health-promoting behaviors (related to food, sleep, physical activity, etc.)**

I strive to empower people of all ages to look beyond the size of their bodies and nourish the person within, with a focus on whole-self wellness. That said, I know it's hard to live in a culture that does not celebrate body diversity.

It can be challenging as a parent not to have anxiety about your children's weight if they do not fall into the socially acceptable range. No one wants their kids to be persecuted and teased because of their bodies. Yet, the way to prevent this is not to prescribe dieting or encourage weight loss. This can confuse the child, as their parents seem to be rejecting their body, too.

Encouraging your child or teen to diet can set them up for a lifetime battle with their body and food. So many of my clients look back at old pictures and wish they could have the body they once thought was "too chubby" or "too big." Often, the child or preteen weight gain that was once feared was a growth spurt that would have evened out if left well enough alone. Often, it's a genetically natural body change that becomes problematic in terms of health or comfort only when the "management" of it starts by dieting or abusing exercise. I can't stress this enough.

Instead of prescribing a diet or weight-loss strategy for your child, I encourage something that might be harder but gives the child some armor against this toxic diet- and weight-oriented culture. **I encourage parents to teach their children body acceptance and that all people come in different shapes and sizes.** There are so many factors that affect body size and weight. No matter what the media says is the favorite shape of the day (and it does change over the decades, history shows us), all bodies are beautiful and miraculous.

I encourage you to have developmentally appropriate conversations with your kids about how some bodies are mistreated in our culture while some are unnecessarily favored. This may not stop any experiences of bullying or mistreatment at school. Still, it might help prevent them from internalizing that mistreatment and feeling like their bodies are *wrong*. If your kids are thin, you can also talk to them about their privilege and not being part of this weight stigma and discrimination.

One study of kids who were bullied or teased because of their weight showed that kids would love more support from their parents. They need to feel that the adults who care about them think their bodies and selves are acceptable. This kind of support is tough to give if you yourself don't believe that all bodies are good bodies. Our popular culture sure doesn't promote this. If you don't feel good about your body or are constantly struggling with food and dieting, it can be hard to wrap yourself around this mentality. Even if you say that all bodies are beautiful or neutral, your child will see you at war with your own size, which will eventually be confusing. I hear this over and over again in the family stories of my clients. It's a generational crisis. Parents have often been victims of some of the same messages and bullying, and we are trying to interrupt the cycle for our children. They are watching.

One of my clients finally stopped a long-standing and dangerous purging behavior when she overheard her nine-year-old say, "Mom eats ice cream, too. She eats a lot of it and then throws up afterward." My client had *no idea* that her daughter was on to her, as she does this eating-disorder behavior in private. She was surprised and mortified to hear this. When she realized that her daughter could imitate her and thought about the damage to her heart, teeth, and esophagus—never mind the social aspects of the behavior—she could see just how terrible and risky the behavior was in herself. She stopped purging cold turkey (which is typically very hard to do) because she saw all too clearly the effect her own eating disorder was potentially having on her child's learning about food. She told her daughter that she had an eating disorder, was getting help for it, and that throwing up after eating is not normal and very unsafe.

Another client noticed her eight-year-old daughter adopting some of her obsessive and quirky ways of eating meals. She was surprised that she noticed and was trying to imitate her at such a young age. Still another client told me that her young son was "shocked" to see his mom eating "two waffles" when she was working on normalizing her eating and allowing for more flexibility. She had no idea that her son was noticing what she ate and noting how different it was from his preferences.

If you are struggling with letting go of diet behavior and focusing on your weight, there is support available. Yes, some individuals have to settle into a larger body to find peace with food. This can be challenging in a culture that values thinness above all other body types right now. I promise you that letting go of thinness as an outcome will bring you so much more freedom and vitality over time. Instead, focus on lifestyle, food, movement, and health-enhancing self-care choices if you indeed care about your health. Focus on pleasure and joy instead of finding fault in the body you have been given in this short life. Weight loss (or gain, if one tends to be underweight when unbalanced) is sometimes a side effect. Still, it needs to be a "back burner" goal, not at the expense of your physical or mental health and well-being.

Suppose you focus on eating, moving, and relating in a balanced, life- and energy-sustaining way. In this case, I believe your health and well-being will improve, no matter your body shape. Many of my fellow nutrition and eating-disorders colleagues have worked with thousands of clients in this non-weight-focused, Health-at-Every-Size (HAES)™ way with much success.

You deserve treatment if you or your child have an eating disorder. Eating disorders run in families. Research has shown that there is a genetic component as well as environmental factors that promote disordered eating. Eating disorders like Anorexia Nervosa (restrictive eating), Bulimia Nervosa (binge/purge cycling), and Binge Eating Disorder (binge-eating without purging) are prevalent and destructive. Despite the emphasis and dialogue about restrictive eating disorders in our culture, the most common eating disorder is Binge Eating Disorder. Most of my clients tend to fall into the category of eating disorder that we call OSFED, Other Specified Feeding and Eating Disorder, and may have features or phases of all the different types.

If your son fears weight gain, he may not feed himself well all day, only to find himself eating frantically at night. If your daughter wishes to be thinner, she may make food choices about calories and not about her own body's wisdom and what it wants. Then she might feel unsatisfied and find herself looking for high-calorie foods later. This is the body's way of protecting itself from starvation. By focusing on weight loss and body shape—instead of balance and nourishment—teens may promote the weight gain they want to abolish. Ironically, trying to lose weight, particularly when your body and brain are still growing (until about age 25), can invite young people into a massive struggle with food and body.

There are many ways in which body size is not determined by how much food we eat. These include differences in metabolism, heredity, hormones, natural patterns of movement, and even something called "epigenetics." The short story on epigenetics around weight is this: how your parents and grandparents ate during your and your mother's conception may affect your tendency to be a particular body shape and size. Seriously. Most interestingly, a study of Dutch famine victims showed that parents who conceived children during this time of starvation went on to have children who were significantly larger-bodied than their siblings. It's as if these kids, whose pregnant mothers didn't have enough to eat, entered the world as caloric-energy conservers, ready for famine. They then grew up in a world where food was no longer insecure but abundantly available, and their genes couldn't adjust.

I sometimes wonder if this isn't one of those less-discussed factors when we hear about "the increased weight of each generation." Could it be that dieting mothers and grandmothers (instructed to do so for health reasons) inadvertently encourage the larger body size in their children that they are trying to avoid? They do this by trying not to gain too much weight in pregnancy and limiting their eating, behaviors that may be carried over from before they were pregnant. Fascinating.

If we humans don't get enough calories to meet biological needs, we don't drop dead (at least not right away); the body simply does what it does more slowly. That's why many chronic restrictive dieters have irritable bowel and constipation on their problem list due to slower digestion. Those with severe anorexia nervosa will have dangerously slow heart rates. Restrictive dieters' hair might get thinner, and women's menstrual periods might stop. When you or your child is not eating enough, hearts keep beating and brains keep functioning. The calories go to the vital body functions but not to the not-so-vital ones, like hair, or fertility, or keeping warm. In a growing body, growth slows, and bones can fail to reach their peak bone density. Caloric deficits can lead to significant health problems later on, but it can be hard to convince a starving teen that something is wrong with starving. She is very much in the present, thinking about teenage stuff, and not worried about debilitating fractures when she is in her 50s.

Restrictive eaters tend to think about food to a distracting degree. They often feel colder than everyone around them, foggy in the head, or exhausted and fatigued. The diet industry wants you to believe it's all about sugar, gluten, or something else you should eliminate. Food allergies and sensitivities are real for some people. Still, I can't tell you how many symptoms of sluggishness, fatigue, lack of focus, and slow digestion go away when clients start eating *more* food—*any* food—*especially* carbohydrates, which diet culture currently vilifies.

Developing bodies do not benefit from elimination diets unless there is a clear anaphylactic-allergic response to some foods or intense allergy symptoms, like hives or skin rashes that go away when the food is eliminated. In children with mild, non-anaphylactic allergies, keeping some low-level exposure (like giving them butter regularly when there is a milk allergy) may lead some children to outgrow their allergy. Other than these kinds of allergy- or sensitivity-related eliminations, most dietary restrictions are just not appropriate for growing young bodies that require various foods to thrive.

When I speak to parent groups, I often tell them that I can turn their children into binge eaters. Parents are then all ears, because they don't want a child who overeats any more than they want to be stigmatized for their own habits. I tell them that the most surefire way to make their child a binge eater is to take away their favorite foods. When those foods become forbidden, they become more attractive or "charged." A cookie is just a cookie when you can have one any time you want. And, yes, kids are very capable of eating cookies moderately. Once they get the idea that cookies are forbidden or "bad"—and this often happens early on—things shift. If parents paint a picture of scarcity and say that cookies are restricted to only particular times or eliminate them from the house, they become more charged. They become cookies with a capital "C."

Yes, this works with grown-ups and food, too. When we're on a diet restriction, there is often a very young part of us that is itching to rebel against the limitation. This rebellious young part in many of us does not like to be deprived and wants the cookies even more now that they are forbidden. It's human nature to want what we can't have and to hoard when we feel deprived or worried that we won't see a loved food again. There is wisdom in that rebellion against restriction, because it's a survival strategy. Creating scarcity as a wellness strategy eventually backfires.

Dieting and food restriction do this, as do poverty and real food insecurity, like when there are not enough food resources to go around a family. Poverty taxes cognitive resources and causes self-control challenges. Many things need to be resisted when you can afford so little. Resisting temptations depletes energy, so poverty makes it hard to make health-giving choices or stop behaviors like smoking or binge eating.

Many financially stable households inadvertently create a scarcity mindset when they keep all processed or sugar-sweetened foods out of the house. Parents may be well-intended, but the child feels that others have more than they do and crave those foods even more. A balanced, moderate approach to stocking the kitchen is preferred. Once kids are old enough to have some say in the grocery list, consulting them about grocery items makes them feel a part of the process and not deprived.

It's also human nature to want to control things when our lives feel a little chaotic—or a lot chaotic, as many modern families will attest. But trying to control food is a recipe for more chaos. The mind wants what it can't have even more. And when the body and brain are starving, the drive to eat and think about food all the time increases. Also, the digestive hormone ghrelin gets secreted when we are emptier than our bodies would like us to be. Ghrelin makes us feel even more hungry. It's the body's natural weight and food regulator, and it tells us it's time to eat. So, when eating restrictively, we have all these forces working against the diet. No wonder it's so hard to eat less food sustainably. In Step 3, we'll look at how to provide for instead of deprive our families' bodies. In Step 4, we'll look at why focusing on *self-care* when making food choices—instead of *self-control*—is the answer to eating in a way that supports a healthy relationship with our bodies.

I want to add that eating disorders are complex emotional disorders that are not just about diet and weight. Individuals with eating disorders are in great pain, using food and their bodies to communicate that. The obsession with food and weight and the cycle of over- and under-eating can take on a life of its own. Even if you don't have a diagnosed eating disorder, you can have a complicated relationship with food. There may be significant underlying emotional struggles (depression, anxiety, obsessive-compulsive disorder, or trauma), and then the wellness-oriented culture we live in fuels the fire.

So, if weight-loss dieting doesn't work (the roughly 96 percent chance you'll gain back any weight you lost is, simply, not good odds), what is the alternative if you or your kids want to feel good in their bodies at the beach this summer? First and foremost, remember to view yourself and your children as whole people (body, mind, and spirit—not just body), and encourage care on all levels. We'll talk about accepting and respecting our amazing, miraculous bodies in the next chapter, Step 2.

As parents, you get to choose your path. Still, I hope I've given you enough reasons to ditch demoralizing dieting and restrictive eating patterns for good—for your own well-being and for your children. Remember that *it's not that you don't have willpower*. Don't let the wealthy wellness industry convince you of that. There are valid reasons why you might not trust your body. Food restriction may be precisely what is making you feel like a failure. Restrictive eating is not sustainable. Our bodies and minds protect us against it by making us want and need to eat. And eat more. Do your body and spirit a favor, and throw out the diet, the scale, and maybe even the bikini you wore when you were 20 that you swear you will get into again someday. Respect your body where it's at, and encourage your children to do the same.

If you need help with a troubled relationship with food, my colleagues and I, who do this kind of non-diet and Intuitive Eating™ nutrition therapy, would be happy to help you practice tuning in, listening, and respecting that inner wisdom that we all have within us. (Look out for any professionals touting Intuitive Eating as a weight-loss method. That is not its intention today.) I encourage you to find health professionals to work with who believe in your body's wisdom. This can be hard to do when there is so much fear of the "obesity epidemic."

Look for dietitians who specialize in disordered eating (CEDRD or CEDS) and doctors and psychotherapists who do not fat-shame or tell you that you need to lose weight for medical problems that are treated differently in those with smaller body sizes. I highly recommend my colleague Christy Harrison's book *Anti-Diet: Reclaim Your Time, Money, Well-Being, and Happiness through Intuitive Eating,* as well as my own book *Nourish: How to Heal Your Relationship with Food, Body, and Self* if you need more guidance around letting go of dieting and building a more intuitive and self-connected style of eating.

Let's summarize the physical and psychological risks of dieting, beyond its tendency to increase weight cycling and struggle over time, as well as encourage a challenging relationship with food.

Physical risks of repeated dietary restriction include:

- Poor nutrition and nutrient deficiencies

- Slow metabolism and digestion

- Fatigue

- Weakness

- Hypertension

- Increased risk of cardiac and cardiovascular problems

- Premature aging with weight cycling and poor nutrition

- Gallstones

Psychological risks of repeated dietary restriction include:

- Obsession with weight

- Heightened responsiveness to external food cues

- Decreased enjoyment of food

- Disordered eating patterns

- Disordered lifestyle (excessive or inadequate exercise, social life affected by avoiding certain eating occasions, etc.)

- Increased incidence of eating disorders

- Increased pressure to conform to society's standards of beauty

- Increased sense of failure

- Decreased self-esteem

- Financial burden

The rest of the steps in this book are designed to help you support your children. Hopefully, they will help you do the same for yourself. The steps in this book aren't meant to be linear. You will probably have to revisit Step 1 many times as you catch yourself making food choices for restrictive reasons or wondering if that food plan your neighbor is following might be good for your family. The next step, *Respect and Speak Well of Your Body*, is also not easy. Still, it's a vital step toward a healthy, loving relationship with your whole self. It's also an invaluable step in encouraging your children to feel good in their bodies.

Step 1: References and Resources

Story, M. and Brown, J.E. "Do young children instinctively know what to eat? The studies of Clara Davis revisited." *The New England Journal of Medicine*. 1987; 316 (2): 103–106.

Berge, J.M., Winkler, N.L., Miller, J., Haynos, A.F., and Newmark-Sztainer, D. "Intergenerational transmission of parent encouragement to diet from adolescence into adulthood." *Pediatrics*. 2018; 141 (4).

Mann, T., Tomiyama, A.J., Westling, E., Lew, A.M., Samuels, B., and Chatman, J. "Medicare's search for effective obesity treatments: diets are not the answer." *American Psychologist*. 2007; 62 (3): 220–233.

Lowe, M. R., Doshi, S. D., Katterman, S. N., and Feig, E. H. "Dieting and restrained eating as prospective predictors of weight gain." *Frontiers in Psychology*. 2013; 4: 577.

Cook-Cottone, C. "Embodied self-regulation and mindful self-care in the prevention of eating disorders." *Eating Disorders.* 2016; 24 (1): 98–105.

Arcelus, J., Mitchell, A.J., Wales, J., and Nielsen, S. "Mortality rates in patients with anorexia nervosa and other eating disorders: a meta-analysis of 36 studies." *Archives of General Psychiatry.* 2011; 68 (7): 724–731.

Hepworth, K. "Eating disorders today—not just a girl thing." *Journal of Christian Nursing.* 2010; 27 (3): 236–243.

The Association for Size Diversity and Health (ASDAH). https://asdah.org/

Himmelstein, M.S. and Puhl, R.M. "Weight-based victimization from friends and family: Implications for how adolescents cope with weight stigma." *Pediatric Obesity.* 2019; 14 (1). doi: 10.1111/ijpo.12453. Epub 2018 Sep 21. PMID: 30241115.

Painter, R.C., Roseboom, T.J., Bleker, O.P. "Prenatal exposure to the Dutch famine and disease in later life: An overview." *Reproductive Toxicology.* 2005; 20: 345–352.

Harrison, C. *Anti-Diet: Reclaim Your Time, Money, Well-Being, and Happiness through Intuitive Eating.* New York, NY: Little, Brown Spark, 2019.

Schauster, H. *Nourish: How to Heal Your Relationship with Food, Body, and Self.* Somerville, MA: Hummingbird Press, 2018.

Harrison, C. *The Wellness Trap: Break Free from Diet Culture, Disinformation, and Dubious Diagnoses, and Find Your True Well-Being.* New York, NY: Little, Brown Spark, 2023.

Sole-Smith, V. *Fat Talk: Parenting in the Age of Diet Culture.* New York, NY: Henry Holt and Company, 2023.

Tribole, E. and Resch, E. *Intuitive Eating: A Revolutionary Anti-Diet Approach (4th edition).* New York, NY: St. Martin's Publishing Group, 2020.

Schwartz, R.C. and Sweezy, M. *Internal Family Systems Therapy (2nd edition).* New York, NY: The Guilford Press, 2020.

Step 2

Respect and Speak Well of Bodies, Including Your Own

(Your Children May Look Like You Someday)

"Mom, you and I are members of the itty
bitty titty committee. Own it."

~ Ava, age 15

Does the title of this chapter make you squirm? If you are
scrolling back in your mind, thinking about all those times
when you bashed your belly or complained about your thighs in
front of your kids, first and foremost, be kind to yourself. Please
forgive yourself for all those times you body-shamed yourself
in front of your children. Of course, you'd never intentionally
body-shame your kid. But please know that when you say negative things about the one body that your kid is most likely to
end up looking like (or looks up to most), then it's confusing.

Nurture

The quote at the start of this Step came from my daughter when I made a disparaging remark about my chest. It was a momentary lapse of reason, for sure. These breasts of mine fed my twin daughters for years, and Ava knew there was nothing wrong with them. The fact that they are small-ish is inconsequential and genetic. She reminded me that our body types are similar and acceptable.

Your babies don't care what the body-shape trend of the day is. I think this is one of the reasons why many of my clients loosen the hold that negative body image has on them if they bring infants into their homes. The young ones appreciate the warm, soft, fleshy bodies that make up their caregivers. They know firsthand that these beings who care for them feel amazing, comforting, and perfect.

Until the culture—or their parents themselves—say otherwise.

Think about how your baby (or another unconditionally loving being, like your pet) loves the *feel* of you and not how you look at your best selfie angle. Very young children are curious about bodies and their different shapes and textures without judgment. They sometimes ask embarrassing questions or call out a very large person, maybe even using the word "fat," but doing so often with reverence, interest, and matter-of-factness. It's only when the culture around children (which is hard to avoid) gives them the idea that fatness or other body qualities are negative that children begin to judge their own bodies—and others'.

Some body comparison is a developmental milestone. At around age five or six, children begin to be aware of physical differences and compare themselves to children around them. They start to look at each other's bellies and measure them, play doctor and explore each other's parts, and enjoy measuring themselves against their peers in various ways. They are examining their feelings and beliefs about their body, hair, and skin. This is a normal process, a social milestone, and part of separation and individuation from parents. There is awareness both of the differences of others and the uniqueness of the self.

There is no need to mess with this stage of development or be mortified if your kid points out your or another's "bouncy belly." They are being curious and appreciating differences. Our own adult judgments often cloud this natural stage of exploration. There's an excellent chance that there is no negative judgment in your children's noticing, even if they use the terms "fat," "big," or "large." When we freak out about these terms and tell them, "It's not nice to point and use that word," we send the subtle-but-powerful message that *fat* and *large* are negative and shameful. Try embracing the word "fat" as a descriptor, like "blue-eyed," "muscular," or "short." If your child calls another child *fat* as a way to be mean, you might respond, "Alex is fat, and there is nothing wrong with that. We know that bodies come in all sizes and shapes. And we accept all people. How boring it would be if we all looked the same."

I invite you to explore your own biases about specific terms and aim to maintain a neutral attitude about these terms and body shapes. This is likely very hard to do if your culture and family taught you to fear these kinds of bodies. Still, it's a mighty end to the oppression of persons in larger bodies if you can respond to your children's curiosity with neutrality, not shame or disgust.

And, as you can imagine, talking about your own body negatively makes your child, who loves you, question the feelings of positive body connection that he has with you. If you hate your body, maybe then your daughter wonders if she should hate it, too—or her own, for that matter. I have had several clients describe to me in some detail a conversation with a parent that made them think that bodies and appetites were to be hated and/or feared. Again, forgive yourself if you've had some moments of this kind of dialogue with your child. Commit to creating a body-appreciating vibe in your house from now on.

Let's talk a little about what is behind some of this body-shaming. Sadly, the medical establishment and the "war on obesity" have created such a fear of bodyfat, large body size, and being unhealthy that we have a term now for people who develop a pathological relationship to being "healthy" and "clean" in their eating and habits: **orthorexia**. When someone is not able to go to a gathering with dear friends because they are fearful of the "unhealthy" foods that would be served, or they think all day about what they are going to cook, when to eat, and when to exercise, all in the name of "healthy living," then it can become quite the opposite. Stress, constriction, and worry about being in or out of control are typically at the core of orthorexia.

Sometimes control strategies like disordered eating result from deeper issues or trauma. **Often orthorexic individuals look like they really have their self-care together—and they**

definitely curate a good-looking feed on social media—but they are typically working hard underneath to compensate for pain and feeling out-of-control or unhappy in other areas of their lives. Often this behavior starts innocently as a move toward health and vitality but then gets lost in compulsive step-counting, body-weighing, and creating the "perfect" meals.

Let's go back to why we require a term like "orthorexia," a newer eating-issue designation coined in 1996 by Dr. Steven Bratman. Way back in Western history, early modern colonialism introduced moralistic ideas about food. Fear of fat bodies has racial and socio-cultural origins. Sabrina String's outstanding book, *Fearing the Black Body*, discusses how "excessive" eating was seen as immoral and more likely to make white, middle-class, Protestant women start to resemble the bodies of African or Irish women. Our modern-day weight oppression developed out of these racist and classist ideas. In the twentieth century, science and medical communities began labeling fat bodies as unhealthy. However, the fad of thinness was well-established before "health" got into the mix. Doctors became influenced by the health- and life-insurance companies that used a measurement that was later called the body mass index, or BMI, to categorize people as "normal weight" (or "ideal weight"), "overweight," and "underweight."

The BMI is (pardon my language) bullshit. It was developed by a Belgian astronomer as a statistical exercise. It was never intended for clinical or medical use. It was created using white Europeans, not accounting for differences in the average body size of others not in that group. In 2013, Flegal and colleagues in the *Journal of the American Medical Association* reviewed several extensive research studies. They determined that "overweight" has the *lowest* mortality risk of any group on the BMI chart. The studies showed that if you fall into the "overweight" category, you are less likely to die from all causes. Why, then, are we calling this "overweight"?

Furthermore, the BMI says nothing about body composition and is ineffective at predicting health outcomes. You can't tell me that my favorite Boston Celtics basketball players are unhealthy. However, the BMI may determine that these dense, muscular athletic bodies are "obese" and at-risk health-wise. On the other side of the spectrum, people of Asian descent, who tend to have smaller bone densities, are often underdiagnosed when they have health issues because the doctors assume their lower weights protect them. Many researchers have recommended that we eliminate this outdated, inaccurate, and racist tool that we've been using over the years.

Many parents also share with me their distress about the emphasis placed on the pediatric growth charts. While the growth patterns depicted help highlight a period of time when a child may be falling off their expected trajectory of growth and could use some attention, we all know that growth does not always happen predictably. In fact, one of my daughters seemed to grow in a slow and steady, gradual way, while the other fraternal twin grew in large spurts around developmental milestones. While it might be helpful in pointing out potential problems, putting too much emphasis on growth charts can make those parents who have kids who don't follow the norms or fall along the 50th percentile feel like something is wrong.

Along with the insurance companies' introduction of the BMI chart, the moralization of food has continued in our history. The formation of a government agency, the Food Administration, as a response to international food shortages after World War I, metaphorically "fed" the trend of viewing food as rule-and-order and moral-based. These new beliefs and ideas challenged food traditions and customs, eventually shaping the nutrition-science field. As a member of this field, I can attest that nutrition science continues to carry oppressive bias regarding research and teaching on weight and health.

So, I'm saying here that it's not your fault that you dis your body sometimes. There is a lot of historical support for that dissing. Still, it does not make it right. It's demoralizing and preoccupying. Body acceptance is the balm that can bring attention back to what is meaningful in one's life. In my first book, *Nourish*, Step 2 is "Body Acceptance, if not Love." I tell my clients they don't have to love every nook and cranny of their bodies. Still, it is essential to accept and appreciate the body they were born with and the wrinkles and scars they have earned from living.

One of the best ways to accept our bodies is to understand that many forces are at work affecting our body size, shape, and health. Heredity, hormones, and lifelong physical-activity patterns (including how naturally mobile and fidgety or grounded and still you are) profoundly affect your body size and shape. During middle childhood and early adolescence, children and young teens develop a sense of self-esteem and individuality, comparing themselves and their bodies with peers. Depression and eating disorders increase in prevalence and seriousness, particularly among females, during this time.

Suppose your child or teen feels terrible in her body and feels she must be smaller than who she is at present (because she has learned from the broader culture and/or her family culture that *smaller is better*). If so, she is more likely to go on a diet. She is also liable to make food choices that reflect restriction rather than pleasure, exercise to exhaustion and not for enjoyment, and walk around with a general sense of being defective and too much.

Sometimes negative body feelings (in you or your family members) are beyond cultural comparisons and may stem from a violation of the body by sexual or physical abuse—or by a history of neglect of one's bodily or emotional needs. Sometimes there are concerns around diverse sexual or gender identity (LGBTQIA+). What one cannot express may be displaced in body or eating issues. When negative body thoughts—and the behaviors that stem from them—become constant, obsessive, and distracting from the rest of life, an eating disorder may develop.

Eating disorders, the number-one killer of all psychiatric illnesses, are complex problems about so much more than food and chasing body perfection. Still, we can't ignore the cultural context in which they flower. How often have you overheard a bunch of people (usually women) criticize their bodies as if this were a way to bond? It's not an accident that eating disorders occur more often in developed countries. In places where food is not plentiful, and survival beats out body-sculpting for the typical pastime, obsession over food and body occurs less.

Step 2

Does your child overhear you saying, "This makes me look fat," or "Oh, she really let herself go"? Does your child overhear you saying, "Oh, I shouldn't eat this," or "I'll have to run this off later"? Diana Rice, a dietitian with Anti-Diet Kids, says, "When you say, 'I can't believe I've gained so much weight! Ugh, I feel gross. I'm going to get my act together this year and lose weight,' kids hear, 'People who gain weight are disgusting and irresponsible. If they try harder, they wouldn't be fat.'" This isn't true and contributes to stigmatizing fat bodies, including the shape your child may have someday.

It may seem like a compliment, but the statement, "Oh, you look so good! Did you lose weight?" is also vicious. Our goodness should not be attached to our body size and shape. While innocent at first glance, these comments can be devastating and promote the idea that someone's worth is connected mainly to appearance.

In fact, some of my clients have comments like these going on in their heads so much all day that it's hard to focus on much else. Others may be able to challenge those thoughts and function well in their lives but still feel a debilitating sense of shame and disgust around their bodies that percolates in the background. Subtle comments about weight to a "chubby" child go destructively deep and erode self-esteem. I hear about this childhood shame in the stories of many of my clients who have struggled with a challenging relationship with food for decades. Negative body thoughts can go awry and become the foundation on which develops a terrible relationship with eating and fitness.

For some, this may ultimately lead to an eating disorder, as the body and food are used to express pain, neglect, sadness, anger, trauma, and a sincere desire (in all of us) to be loved and accepted.

Perhaps you are reading this book because you struggle with disordered eating and don't want to pass it on to your children. **I invite you to reframe how you talk to yourself (and those around you) about body weight and shape. This is one of the most important things you can do to prevent eating disorders and body shame in your family and your greater community.**

I work with truly beautiful, inside and out, people of all genders who do not like their bodies and themselves. These are successful, intelligent, funny, articulate, creative, and uniquely gifted individuals—but they cannot see it because all they see is how "fat" they are. It doesn't matter what size they are, either. Their medical charts may say "overweight" or "underweight" (and we now know what bullshit those BMI-connected terms are). What matters to them most is that they feel less than their *whole selves* because of how their bodies look.

What happens when negative body thoughts go all wrong? Who doesn't have them once in a while? How does this thinking get out of control and develop into eating disorders for some and not others? There are so many genetic, temperamental, and environmental factors that predispose some people to eating disorders. I've noticed frequently that problematic eating and bad body thoughts become a way to take feelings and make them concrete. "I don't like myself" becomes easier to articulate if she says, "I don't like my body." "Something is not right in my life" becomes "Something is not right in my body."

If we don't like our bodies, the health influencers on social media say that we can do all kinds of things to change them. It's an area of our lives that we are told we can have control over. But all the green smoothies and CrossFit in the world won't make us like ourselves any more, compensate for painful feelings we need to express, or make what feels wrong about our lives disappear. The diet and wellness industries feed our children (and ourselves) the story that, if we just change our bodies, we can feel good and change our lives. It's really *not* that simple. We actually *don't* have that much control over our bodies.

Some of my clients "lose the weight," usually for a short time, and realize they don't feel much better about themselves. How devastating to find out that losing weight, something that was chased for decades, is not the answer to lifelong happiness. They often realize that the "better" life in a "better" body is a pretty shallow life—one which their deeper, more authentic selves aren't so interested in living.

Now, please know that I'm not bashing self and body care. I'm a dietitian/nutritionist, embodiment therapist, and dancer. I believe in taking care of the fantastic vessels that we are blessed to inhabit in our lifetimes. I consider the body as one of our modes of self-expression. I work on helping my clients appreciate the beautiful part of us that the body is. As a Somatic Experiencing (SE)™ practitioner, I believe that inhabiting and listening to the body is absolutely important in healing from trauma. However, our bodies are just *one part* of who we are. I might make a body connection when I dance with a partner, and that's lovely. Still, it's the people I make heart-and-soul connections with who nourish me on a deep level and keep me dancing with others in community.

Accepting (and maybe even loving) our bodies—and teaching our kids to accept and love theirs—starts, in my opinion, with loving ourselves and with seeing our bodies as an extension of that self-love. After hundreds of discussions with clients recovering from eating disorders over the decades, I have this opinion. **I want to challenge you to ask yourself the following questions when you say something negative (out loud or in your mind) about your body. Ask yourself, "How am I feeling inside?" and "What's really not feeling good right now?"**

Try it. Are those lousy body thoughts coming up because you feel inadequate after talking to someone you admire? Are they coming up because you are feeling judged by a family member? Are you "feeling fat" (which, by the way, is not a feeling) because your dieting friend is ordering the burger without the bun, and you are wondering if you should, too? Getting in touch with deeper feelings of shame, inadequacy, fear, loneliness, exhaustion, and grief that might be under those negative body thoughts is tougher. The body is an excellent container for our negative energy.

When you feel bad about your body and ask yourself, "What's really going on right now?" you may get to what you are feeling in the present moment. When doing so, you may be less likely to use food or exercise self-destructively. And you are less likely to pass on these habits to the young people around you. Over time, I have watched many parents substitute the destructive eating behavior (binge eating or consciously going hungry, for example) with something that more adequately addresses the feelings underneath. After careful reflection, some of my clients have noticed that they use food restriction, binge eating, purging, or hyper-exercise as a self-punishment. They really do feel terrible about themselves, and these behaviors make their internal struggle concrete and real. They embody their pain.

Once you notice what might be behind your negative body thoughts and eating behaviors, examine what doesn't feel right—either on your own or with a trusted friend or therapist. Don't succumb to body bashing just because it's socially acceptable. **We can't even begin to take good care of our bodies and teach our kids to do the same if we hate our bodies or loathe the person within.** I don't find that clients can make a lot of headway in their nutrition therapy or build and sustain self-care practices if they do not understand and care for their deeper, unique selves. Get help with body acceptance if this seems tough to do on your own. It's worth examining some painful truths to eventually reach a place of body neutrality and self-love. I also believe it's one of the most valuable gifts you can give a child in your care.

Eating from a place of self-care and not self-control yourself is important for your children. They see you eat. You can make them the most balanced, healthy meal. Still, if they don't see their parent sitting down and eating that exact same balanced meal, they will be confused about how to feed themselves well. Virginia Sole-Smith states, "It's not 'healthy' to deprive yourself of nourishing food to the point that you want to pick the leftovers off your child's plate. It's not 'healthy' to feed our kids so differently from how we feed ourselves. And that's true for all parents, not just thin parents."

When you teach your kids that feelings are acceptable and part of life (more on that in Step 9), then you give them the tools to tolerate feelings and not express them through the body. **Eating disorders, physical pain, and illness can contain somatically displaced emotions.** We know this because many gastrointestinal conditions, environmental sensitivities, and psychological conditions lessen or even resolve when the genuine emotions stuck in the body get space, time, and support in somatically-oriented therapies.

I recommend that you remove not only body-bashing dialogue but also the scale from your house. It's too easy for kids to get into obsessive-compulsive weighing and to put too much meaning on that number, particularly at a time when their weight fluctuates and increases dramatically at times during growth spurts. Read about it if you aren't familiar with the Health-at-Every-Size (HAES)™ movement. Find health practitioners, if you can, that know about HAES and practice with it foundationally. You'll find more HAES therapists and nutritionists in the eating-disorders field. Still, finding medical doctors and specialists versed in HAES can be difficult, though the numbers are increasing. These clinicians believe that all bodies are worthy of care, regardless of health status, and do not see weight loss as a treatment for most health conditions.

Research supports the fact that changes in health are related to changes in behavior, not weight. Yes, weight's role in health is exaggerated. Research studies (and reporters in the mainstream media) so often connect the two because the *habits* often associated with health problems (eating beyond fullness repeatedly, sedentary lifestyle, etc.) are correlated with the highest weight categories. Correlation is not causation. The *habits and not the weight* are linked to health problems.

There are statistical ways to control different factors in research. When we look carefully at the studies, controlling for the health effects of physical activity, weight's impact on health goes away. So, yes, you can be fat and fit and have a longer, healthier, more vibrant life than a thin person who does not engage in regular exercise. Again, despite all the coverage of the "war on obesity," people in the "overweight" (BMI 25–30) category have the longest lifespan. As I said earlier, why are we calling these people "overweight"? If you haven't ditched the BMI in your mind as a useful health tool, I hope you will now.

Please don't believe the hype and pass it down to your children. **Thin does not buy your kids any more disease-free years, particularly if your body is not naturally conditioned to be thin. What it can do is encourage a lifetime of obsessing that limits one's ability to be really present in relationships and life**.

So, what do you do if you have a larger-bodied child and don't want them to be painfully teased or oppressed by society? I am sure this is why well-meaning parents put kids on diets, even though they ultimately do harm. "Thin privilege" is real in this culture. I know that I have it. I've had some brave clients say, "How do you know what it feels like to be very large and looked down upon because of your size?" They're right; I don't. No amount of reading about size discrimination allows me to wear the shoes of someone living it. I have heard literal horror stories of oppression and cruelty experienced by persons living in larger bodies in this culture. *Why wouldn't you want to shield your child from this?*

Hopefully, by this point, you understand that making weight and shape an issue—and especially trying to change them through diet—do more harm than good. As I've said, many of my clients look back on old photos. They wonder how they ever felt uncomfortable in their very "normal" bodies. A lifetime of fighting with food and their weight has taken them even farther from being connected to their bodies. They'd give anything to return to that body they hated in their teens. Through careful work and reflection, they eventually discover that the problem was not their bodies from the beginning. They felt insecure and awkward, like all teens. They somehow thought that "managing" their body size and shape would make them more acceptable and lovable.

It didn't. At least not in the long term.

If your child is exhibiting fears about being teased or oppressed, I invite you to say, "There are a lot of systems that make you feel that way. It's hard to be in a large body or a queer body in our culture. It's not a value in our family to contribute to this discrimination. We want to treat others—and ourselves—differently."

Please don't feed the monster that says life improves if your body is perfect. **Sure, you may get more attention from peers who are also feeding on the images of the "perfect body," but the routines and self-absorption that are required to maintain perfection throughout one's lifespan take away so**

many more meaningful aspects of life: authentic relation-ships, unbridled joy, and daily ease to name a few. Chasing a "better" body, particularly one that is not natural for your child or family, is just not worth it. Trust me (and hundreds of my clients) on this one.

What would it be like if we put on a bathing suit and our kids heard us say, "Oh, look. I put on a little winter weight this year. Well, that can happen. I guess I need to find a new bathing suit," or, "Well, by mid-summer, after running around outside, I might fit into it, but I'm not attached to it"? No judgment, just matter-of-factly owning that bodies sometimes fluctuate, especially if you live where the seasons do, too. Having a little winter weight on makes sense to keep you warm.

Don't we all wish for our kids to know the truth—that, deep down, you (and they) are the same beautiful people, despite body fluctuation? The only way to communicate this truth is to be more neutral about weight and body size for yourself and others. Treat it like eye color, and don't attach any morality or virtue to it.

We all want to feel good in our bodies. We all want to have vitality and strength and lightness of being. Putting too much emphasis on whether or not we fit into a pair of jeans or a bathing suit is a recipe for low self-esteem and a troubled relationship with food and exercise. If you look in the mirror and feel "less than," don't say that to your child. Do get help with seeing yourself as a whole person. Take everything in your closet that doesn't fit you and donate it, consign it, or give it to a friend who will wear it. Don't hold onto anything that makes you feel less than the stellar being you are. Wear things that make you feel good and express something about yourself. Always remember that you are so much more than the size of your clothes. We all know that a pretty house is delightful, but that alone does not make a happy home.

If you have a child who struggles with low self-esteem (because of teasing or any other reason), help them make a list of things that they or others appreciate about them. Compliment them, but be careful about those compliments being mostly about appearance or the body. Help them notice their sense of humor, kindness to others, or creative ideas. **If you view your child—and yourself—as a whole, interesting person and not just a body, they are more likely to feel that way, too.**

In summary, how do we help our kids accept their bodies and selves and respect those of others?

- Remind them that people come in all different shapes, colors, and sizes and that bodies change significantly over their lifespan. Normalize roundness as part of growth.

- Encourage health and well-being for the whole person, not for producing a particular body type. Don't forget that pleasure and ease are health-promoting, too.

- Don't tolerate fat-shaming in any form, and don't encourage it by overtly or subtly favoring a specific body type in your children.

- Don't talk negatively about your own body, as this confuses your child. Get help with body acceptance if you find this hard to do.

- Let your kids see you enjoying food with them, which is the most crucial lesson in "healthy eating" we can provide as parents.

Step 2: References and Resources

Eccles, J. S. "The Development of Children Ages 6 to 14." *The Future of Children*. 1999; 9(2): 30–44.

McComb, S.E. and Mills, J.S. "Orthorexia nervosa: A review of psychosocial factors." *Appetite*. 2019; 140: 50–75.

Bratman, S. and Knight, D. *Health Food Junkies: Orthorexia Nervosa: Overcoming the Obsession with Healthful Eating*. New York, NY: Broadway Books, 2004.

Strings, Sabrina. *Fearing the Black Body: The Racial Origins of Fat Phobia*. New York, NY: New York University Press, 2019.

Flegal, K. M. *et al.* "Association of All-Cause Mortality with Overweight and Obesity Using Standard Body Mass Index Categories: A Systematic Review and Meta-analysis." *Journal of the American Medical Association*. 2013; 309(1).

Instagram Account: Diana Rice and Anti-Diet Kids. https://www.instagram.com/anti.diet.kids/

Menzel, J. "Avoidant/restrictive food intake disorder: assessment and treatment." In L.K. Anderson, S.B. Murray, and W.H. Kaye (eds.), *Clinical Handbook of Complex and Atypical Eating Disorders*. London: Oxford University Press, 2018.

Schauster, H. *Nourish: How to Heal Your Relationship with Food, Body, and Self.* Somerville, MA: Hummingbird Press, 2018.

Sole-Smith, V. *The Eating Instinct: Food, Culture, Body Image, and Guilt in America.* New York, NY: Henry Holt and Company, 2018.

Association for Size Diversity and Health (ASDAH). https://asdah.org/

Somatic Experiencing (SE) International. https://traumahea ling.org/

STEP 3
Provide, Don't Deprive

"Mom, I live a deprived life. At sixteen,
I am just discovering Pop-Tarts."

~ Kyla, age 16

Yes, my daughter is exposing me in the quote above. I'm a mom who aims to provide lots of different kinds of snacks in the house. I don't diet and have never thought of myself as being overly health-focused in my food choices, though I can't unlearn my nutrition education and strive for balance in what I offer my kids. I aim to make all foods neutral for my family by not making anything off-limits. That said, it's absolutely true that I did not buy Pop-Tarts during my kids' childhood.

My partner tells me this is good, for he subsisted on Pop-Tarts for about a decade. He told me he didn't think that was his best life choice.

Kyla and Ava had a "Where have you been all my life?" experience with Pop-Tarts at age 16, trying every flavor. I found it hysterical because they both had great relationships with food and didn't tend to obsess over anything. Sure, they have their favorite foods, but I never saw them eat to the point of discomfort much. (Well, there was that *one time* Kyla ate a lot of her chocolate mousse birthday cake and fell extremely ill. She still talks about it.)

Generally, though, the Halloween candy rots once the novelty wears off in our house. Even favorite baked goods often aren't eaten before they get stale. We consider cookies delicious and fun foods, and my teens are fantastic bakers, but since cookies are not "special," they get "old" after the first three or four.

My partner and I have more "food baggage" and may eat sweets to the point of discomfort more than my daughters do. I have some weird hoarding tendencies because I'm one of seven siblings. I learned that the yummy thing might disappear if I didn't eat it now. Many adults have genuine food insecurity due to poverty or neglect, deprivation from dieting, or elimination diets in their history. Often patterns of real or imagined food insecurity are passed down through the generations.

All of these can create a drive toward eating certain foods that is more significant than the attuned eater. I'm seeing this more and more in young clients who develop disordered eating after being put on the latest, trendiest diet: gluten- and dairy-free. It's one thing if your child has celiac disease and truly cannot digest gluten (the protein in wheat) without health consequences—or a dairy allergy that leads to rashes or respiratory distress. Those are symptoms that kids can understand as negative consequences of eating a particular food group; avoiding those foods is indeed good care.

The problem occurs when kids don't have life-threatening or life-limiting food allergies or sensitivities but are put on special diets by well-meaning parents for health-enhancing reasons. Of course, the parents don't mean harm and believe they are doing the best for their children. It's heartbreaking, though, to hear from a mom that she thought she was helping her daughter by cutting out gluten and dairy, only to encourage her child to have an intense "charge" around those foods, leading to eventual frantic eating behavior.

I am sharing stories about my children and clients. These are for the purpose of providing real-life examples of the concepts I am presenting. I realize that there are many complicated issues for children with food, and these examples don't necessarily reflect the incredibly hard and painful journey that feeding your child can become. However, if these concepts resonate at all, perhaps it will inspire you to get support from a nutrition therapist on how to talk with your children around eating.

When I started to work with Amelia, she was beginning to understand why her nine-year-old Sophie was so obsessed with food, particularly bread and cheese. Amelia reflected on the way she eliminated many forms of gluten and dairy from Sophie's diet at a young age. Amelia thought it would help her family's digestion, mood, and long-term health if she exposed them to less dairy and gluten, even though they didn't have documented allergies. All the health-oriented rhetoric on the internet said so. It was becoming easier to eliminate foods containing gluten and dairy because all of the other moms in her social circle were doing it, too.

Sophie was an active kid, and she grew rapidly. Once she hit puberty, she got tired of being on the "special allergy diet" at school and asked if she could "just eat mac and cheese" like her peers. Amelia, an intelligent mom who didn't want to create any power struggles around food, said, "Of course." Now she's worried for her daughter because Sophie seems obsessed with bread and cheese and tends to eat beyond fullness until she has a stomachache. She nearly panics on her way to dance class if her mom doesn't have a snack for her and often says, "Did you bring me a snack? Is this all? I told you I'm *really* hungry."

A food-scarcity mindset showed up, indicating that Sophie doesn't believe she will have enough to eat—or that somebody will take care of her. Possibly, Sophie's nervous system struggles to regulate during transitions, and food has become grounding for her, as it is for many of us. The year of deprivation on the "allergy diet," while other kids ate "normal" lunches with cheese and bread, may have fueled some of this "charge" around food. The Covid-pandemic lockdown also led to Sophie seeking food for comfort and when bored.

We all want to feel taken care of and like we have enough. Kids sometimes show signs of hoarding food to compensate for food scarcity (real or imagined or innocently imposed by adults). They also sometimes crave, collect, and hide food because it's soothing and grounding during moments of overthinking or anxiety. Remember that food has represented care and comfort since our first days after birth. Eating and love are entwined, whether we want them to be or not, so when we have some challenges with feeling loved or cared for, enter food as a soother. It's not a problem to eat for comfort, but if food is frequently standing in for emotional expression or more effective ways to cope with challenges in life, then the child may be missing out. I'll write more about this in Step 9, when discussing kids and their feelings.

I haven't been able to tease out what part of Sophie's relationship with food is related to using food to soothe anxiety and what is related to having some well-meaning-but-meaningful food deprivation as a child on the gluten-free, dairy-free diet. She will untangle this as she learns other ways to soothe herself when transitioning from one activity to another. She will hopefully re-learn to eat intuitively, listening to her own body's desires (over others') and appreciating when her body has genuinely had enough.

My now-teenage daughters have never really shown signs of having "charge" around food—until they discovered Pop-Tarts, and clearly much too late in life. I ate Pop-Tarts freely in my youth and currently think they taste like cardboard. I didn't think my kids were missing anything; they weren't as trendy and mainstream in my kids' young lives as they were in the 1980s. But they became a food trend again recently, and I could see they were a delicacy to a teen who had never experienced this sweet, warm comfort food. I guess I thought I was doing my kids a favor by having bagels, eggs, sausages, and oatmeal for breakfast. I'm sorry they felt deprived of the Pop-Tart experience, and I'm glad they're enjoying them now. (I don't even mind being teased about it.)

I'd also like to highlight that my daughters may be unique in their laid-back relationship to food and body. Many parents who have healthy relationships themselves and aim not to deprive their kids may still have children who seem to want sugar all the time. Sweet foods—and many other types of packaged foods—are marketed to young (and older) people in ways that capitalize on the palate and visual interests of the consumer. After all, food companies' number-one priority is business and making money, so it makes sense to make foods attractive to young people and caregiving consumers. Sweets are also often craved when a child is not eating adequately throughout the day. Quick sugar is satisfying and soothing to a belly that is over-hungry or a body that is going through a significant growth spurt.

Keep this in mind if you see children going for lots of sweets. They may not be getting enough calories or carbohydrates from other foods, choosing what works fast and feels good in the moment. Help them by making a variety of snack foods available. Setting some reasonable limits around sweets and desserts also makes sense to some families, as long as every member of the family abides, so that certain siblings don't feel more singled out than others. Consistency without rigidity is the most important factor here, not the actual amount of sweet treats decided on. I like to err on the side of little to no food rules, but I have worked with families where coming up with some agreed-upon limits truly decreased a complicated dynamic around food that was already present.

In the early 1990s, when I was studying nutrition, I had the pleasure of seeing pioneer dietitian and therapist Ellyn

Satter speak at my college. She introduced me to the gold standard "rule" about encouraging children to eat well. She discussed the division of responsibility when we are feeding our kids. It is so simple. **Your responsibility as parents and caregivers is to provide a variety of nutritious food. Your child's responsibility is to eat it.** Yes, this sounds easy, but it's not as simple as it may seem in practice.

Her precise words back then are still relevant in the way we teach parents to feed children today. When we try to move into our kids' lanes and "get" them to eat certain things (or not eat certain things) by coercion, reward, cooking special, separate meals, or doing somersaults in the kitchen, then we are crossing a boundary. We are not helping our children develop appetite-reading and self-regulation skills.

Children must learn what feels good and what doesn't feel good in their bodies *from the inside out*. This is a body-sensing and not a "thinking" function. When forces outside children tell them what or how to eat, they may lose contact with that essential inner regulatory experience that tells them when they are hungry or when enough is enough.

"When I eat a bagel sandwich at breakfast, I have more energy at school."

"When I don't have a snack after school, I have a hard time focusing on my homework."

"I like eating fresh fruit more than dried fruit. It quenches my thirst, and I like the juiciness."

"I get a warm, fuzzy feeling when I eat (insert favorite food)."

These are all examples of body-sensing and not mind-thinking about food. Tuning in to our body sensations is something that we develop over our childhood, but it can also be "unlearned" when we think too much about the nutritional implications of what we are eating.

This doesn't mean we set kids free in a candy store without limitations. As I said above, some limits around sweets are acceptable, for example, as long as everyone in the house follows them. "Here's two dollars for the candy store," or providing a small bag to be filled in that candy store are two reasonable limits. However, cutting out sugar entirely is a recipe for a kid who eats frantically at their friends' houses by middle school. I've seen it! (My daughters' Halloween candy would get dusty, but some of their friends from sugar-free households would hunt for it months later.)

Take your feeder job seriously. Grocery shop, plan meals, and stock the kitchen with variety to support the growth and development of your children. Get help with any of those steps, if you need it and can afford it. If you need help judging what is normal for a child to eat at different stages of development, my colleagues in pediatric nutrition have resources for you. Jill Castle and Maryann Jacobsen have written books (one listed at the end of this chapter) on planning balanced meals that meet children's shifting developmental needs. And I always recommend Ellyn Satter's books, particularly *Secrets of Feeding a Healthy Family* (also listed at this chapter's end).

Young children need the foods put onto their plates, but older children (and you know your child better than any other) may be able to master choosing a variety of foods "family style" from larger dishes at the table. I recommend moving to this kind of self-selection around food as soon as the child can. It's ideal and promotes body and appetite trust. Offer foods from all the different food groups on the table, but don't get too worked up about how much the children eat or whether they eat from each food group. Individual preferences are important, and most children naturally gravitate to a balance from each major food group over a week.

We'll talk more about picky eating in Step 4, but please know that some pickiness or food "jagginess" is normal for many kids. It's common for children to have long periods with a limited palate. Some kids are more sensitive and "pickier" than others. As one of my clients recently said, "Everyone used to make a big deal about how my brother only ate beige foods (pasta, toast, cereal, etc.), but now that he's a grown-up, he's the most adventurous eater of all of us. He's the one having the fancy duck on the menu." Most pickiness is grown out of, mainly if parents don't make much of it. Sometimes responding to pickiness with anxiety or anger turns it into a power struggle—something to exert newfound independence around. Sometimes it's a hallmark of a more significant problem around sensory integration or ARFID (I'll bring this up in Step 5), but most often, it's not.

My fabulous research intern Julianna reviewed the findings from studies and from clinical practitioners who work with children for me while I was writing this chapter. Looking at her research and the writings from pediatric nutrition and health experts, we determined that children may need to try a food 12 to 30 times before accepting it into their palate and liking it. This is why parents shouldn't push—but also shouldn't give up on—new or initially rejected foods. When your child says, "I hate carrots; I tried them already," one thing you might say is, "You know, I didn't used to like green beans, either, but I had to try them a number of times before I got a taste for them. Would you be willing to try just a little bit of carrot tonight to see if you might get your taste buds used to it over time?" If your child says, "Absolutely not," then pick your battles, continuing to offer the food here and there. Chances are that, when your child is offered a rejected food at a friend's house, it may be better received. Palates tend to open up as children get more open to social and other experiences, too.

Some children are more open to new foods and new experiences than others, which can be related to sensory processing, differing taste buds, and temperament. If you have a cautious, risk-averse child, he may not be open to green veggies or gristly meat. It might take many tries and years before he's okay with them, if ever. Being as nonchalant about this as possible, while continuing to expose him to all kinds of different foods at the table, will make this trial-and-error process go more smoothly.

Force-feeding or coercive techniques to "finish your veggies" or "eat something green" usually result in that food being repelled more. The same goes for saying one food is "bad" versus another. Sometimes kids crave foods because there's a lot of energy around avoiding them. **Generally, parents should**

present food as neutral, with no moral imperative. When this occurs, children naturally choose a well-balanced diet over days or weeks. This can be hard to do when our "clean-eating" culture sends these messages of food morality to all of us.

Don't impose food rules on your child. Ideally, don't have them yourself. I talked about this in Step 1 when I addressed dieting. If you set rigid rules, your child may use food to separate and individuate from you during the teen years. You will have plenty of other things to negotiate then, like curfews and when they get to borrow the car. Ideally, food should not be a battleground and a place where a teen finds "control." As Diana Rice of Anti-Diet Kids says, "Your kids need unlimited experiences with sugar to understand how it feels in their bodies and make their own decisions about how much to have. If someone else is always making those decisions for them, when they reach adulthood, there's a good chance they'll have no idea how to manage this."

My rule of thumb around meals, a simple nutrition lesson for kids and adults alike, is that a balanced meal includes some grain, some protein, some fat, some produce, and some pleasure. It's really that simple. Teaching older kids what makes a protein (meats, fish, milk/cheese, nuts, and legumes) and what it does (gives energy and builds muscles) is usually all the nutrition education they need about each food group. Some kids are very interested in health, nutrition, and their bodies and may ask questions. In that case, you can give them some more information and explain that carbohydrates, proteins, and fats are the "gasoline" or "energy" that keeps us going, while vitamins and minerals are like the spark plugs in a car engine that help everything work correctly when there's enough energy around.

Telling kids they need carbohydrates for energy and brain power is particularly important now, when social-media messages about carbs tend to be negative. (In the 1970s and '80s, the diet villain was fats, but today it's carbs.) Most of the time, though, kids are only marginally interested in nutrition science and find talking about their body sensations of hunger and their favorite food preferences much more enjoyable.

Prioritize family meal time. I know this is hard when schedules don't match and taxiing kids to after-school activities gets in the way. It can be even more complicated in dual-income and single-parent families. It's hard to prepare and sit down to meals in today's modern, busy world. Try your best to eat together, whether it's homecooked or takeout or anything in between—at least most of the evening meals during the week, even if it's later or earlier than it makes sense. Research shows that kids' mental health improves exponentially with more family meals.

Make sure those meals are not full of conflict and argument, too. Some natural expression of feelings is healthy and good, but try not to have the dinner table be a battlefield. Aim to cultivate a peaceful and supportive environment around the table, where everyone feels heard and tummies can relax and digest well. I have had numerous clients cite chaotic, boisterous dinner meals as connected to why they don't have a taste for sitting down and eating regularly. Their eating has become dysregulated because their eating experience was never pleasant, and their digestion was never smooth.

Regular meals and snacks help your child develop a predictable hunger and satiety pattern. Teach by example that regular eating is vital for fuel and well-being. However, don't make any meal or snack pattern rigid, so that the child's body remains the primary decision-maker around eating. If it's snack time and your child is not hungry for a snack, don't push it. If he comes back an hour later and asks for a snack, and it's not too close to the next meal, then trust that he knows when he's hungry and offer a snack then.

Children and teens often need snacks to consume enough energy calories for growth and brain development. Going longer than 3–5 hours without something to eat often creates "hangry" kids, where blood sugar is crashing, affecting their mood. One of my daughters would come home from grade school very overstimulated, tired, and cranky. She couldn't focus on her homework and would be in tears. I would suggest that maybe her body was hungry, and she would check in (if she wasn't too "hangry" and dysregulated to do so). Often, all she needed was a snack, ideally something containing some carbohydrate, protein, and fat (think toast with peanut butter or an apple with cheese). She settled down and could magically focus on her homework after eating a snack most of the time.

Involve kids in food preparation and selection. Children generally get excited about being a part of the family meal-planning process. They are building good skills that our schools don't teach much (how to plan and execute feeding oneself and a family). When kids take ownership in the process, there are fewer power struggles around meals. This makes sense, as they are part of choosing meals and not just being "made" to eat what adults prepare.

I encourage you to do this more often as the children you eat with get older. Katherine, one of my clients, said this family meal-planning process became one of their most joy-filled regular practices. The children got excited about it being "their meal" night, and it took a lot of guesswork out of preparing dinner, keeping it from being a last-minute decision when mom was depleted. The whole family got more involved in cooking, eating, and planning.

Feeling secure in having enough food to satisfy young tastes and appetites can help children feel cared for. True food insecurity in families who are struggling financially can trickle down to create disordered eating or hoarding behaviors around food. I see this repeatedly in the histories of many of my clients. Sometimes food choices are limited. When individuals and families take advantage of food assistance programs, it can go a long way toward helping children and adults feel a sense of security. Some cities and towns have more opportunities and access to quality food than others. I've observed that Canada does a better job than the U.S. around access to community meals for everyone, no questions asked. Governing bodies in all countries need to continue to prioritize access to a variety of food for all families, regardless of income, and doing so in a way that does not increase shame.

When kids experience deprivation around food—either because snacks are not allowed, certain food groups or types are not allowed, or other restrictions are placed around variety in their diets—it can encourage secretive and frenetic food

behavior. I sadly hear about this repeatedly, often from those who come from homes where the parents meant well and just wanted the family to eat "healthfully."

I want to take a moment or two to discuss other forms of either subtle or overt deprivation that often get tangled up with problematic food behaviors. Many people with frantic- or compulsive-eating behaviors describe situations when their needs were not met in childhood. As human beings, we all have solid needs for love, belonging, emotional closeness, touch, warmth, affection, and attention. Children don't need these things all the time. In fact, it can be smothering and intrusive to some children to have too much touch and attention. This is where knowing your unique child well is helpful. Some kids want to come home from school and decompress from the social stimulation; going to their rooms and having quiet time is resourcing for them. Some kids want to connect with a loved one and process by talking about their day. Some need physical activity before settling down to do homework or connect with others.

I invite you to consider the children in your care and their various needs. Are these being met regularly? Quality is more important than quantity in most cases. A greeting with eye contact and a hug (if your child likes hugs), asking them about their day (and respecting their desire to be alone or sit quietly in the car, decompressing) shows that you are attuned to their needs and care about them. If you have difficulty figuring out what your child needs, ask them. They may not be able to articulate that they need a hug or a snack or to talk about the events of the day, but just asking shows that their caregiver does care. When the caregivers care, that care will be internalized and show up as good self-care once the child is old enough to practice it.

Children learn by imitation. The child who spends time around a constantly working parent who never stops to check in with themselves or their loved ones, sadly, learns to work and underappreciate self-care continually. The child who never has touch or emotional affection modeled doesn't understand how to give or receive it well. On the extremes, a child who experiences physical, emotional, or sexual abuse from a caregiver grows up with a very insecure attachment system and often feels confused and unable to effectively care for themselves or others without examining this attachment system and doing repair work. Some of this work may include attaching to safer, more predictable others, often in psychotherapy settings.

I write all of this, as a parent myself, with so much compassion. Sometimes we have to work two or more jobs to make ends meet and can't be around our children as much as we'd like. Single parenting and work obligations often make it hard to be as present to our children's needs as we would like. Quality time is more important than quantity. Letting kids know that we wish we could play with them more, but we also have to work to make sure that we all have good food to eat, too. Statements made about reality will go a long way, especially if they are said with neutrality, love, and connection.

We all know that it takes a village. Having safe, warm, consistent adults in and around our children's lives helps incredibly. (This is why our teachers and daycare providers should not be paid so much less than sports figures—but don't get me started.) I know firsthand that parenting is a job that can bring us to our knees and often brings out all of our wounded younger parts. We say things we don't mean. We fight, flee, or freeze when our kids really need us to stay grounded. We fail to be there at times when they need us.

Well, guess what? **We are not perfect, and our kids don't want us to be perfect. (That's a rather lofty standard to live up to.) They benefit from seeing us striving to be the best caregivers and selves we can be.** This means being as present as we are able (remember, quality versus quantity), apologizing for obvious missteps, and taking responsibility for the times when we become aware that we may not have been meeting emotional or physical needs. The latter goes a long way toward repairing small or large wounds in a child's world. The adults who are growing and doing their own work inspire children to also grow in a connected and effective way.

If you struggle with your young wounds from childhood, feel challenged to take good care of yourself, or find yourself not behaving the way you'd like to around your kids, then do some soul-searching and prioritize healing, seeking professional help from a psychotherapist or other trusted healer. Be compassionate with yourself. You will better recognize and meet your children's needs when attending to your own first and foremost. It's nearly impossible to support those we love if we don't have enough internal and external support in our own lives.

Prioritizing self-care and not being afraid to reach out and get help from any number of sources will go a long way toward giving your children a strong foundation. As they gradually take care of themselves increasingly with age, they will do so with fewer bumps because they've had great role models who weren't afraid to take good care of themselves. Feeding ourselves well, relating to other humans, and finding balance in life are skills that develop over time. The foundations come from our families of origin and the surrounding community.

In summary, I invite you to take your Caregiver and Feeder job seriously. Then, sit back, and let your children do the eating and growing.

- Plan meals enough to make sure that regular eating happens. Stock the kitchen and table with a variety of foods that support growth.

- Stay in your own lane and never force, coerce, or significantly limit food. Life-threatening or life-limiting allergies are an exception.

- Remember that new foods may need to be tried 12 to 30 times before acceptance. A neutral response to a kid's food refusal and continued exposure will eventually lead to a growing palate. Avoid power struggles by being nonchalant but regular in introducing new foods.

- Prioritize family meal times, and make them as peaceful as possible.

- Controlling and restricting food is associated with rebound overeating in children (and adults). We often crave what we can't have, so don't create unwanted food insecurity or a scarcity mentality by limiting your kids' options.

- Involve children and teens in the process of selecting and preparing food for the family.

- Stay attentive to your children's needs for love, belonging, emotional closeness, touch, warmth, affection, and attention. Sometimes, when there are deficits in these areas, people look to food (either the hoarding of it or the control of it) to fill the void. Food represents love and care—and has since our first baby breaths on this planet—so this makes sense.

Step 3: References and Resources

Satter, E. *Secrets of Feeding a Healthy Family: How to Eat, Raise Good Eaters, How to Cook.* Madison, WI: Kelcy Press, 2008.

Satter, E. *Child of Mine: Feeding with Love and Good Sense.* Boulder, CO: Bull Publishing, 2000.

Castle, J. and Jacobsen, M. *Fearless Feeding: How to Raise Healthy Eaters from High Chair to High School.* Fearless Feeding Press, 2018.

Carruth, B.R. and Skinner, J.D. "Revisiting the picky-eater phenomenon: neophobic behaviors of young children." *Journal of the American College of Nutrition.* 2000; 19(6): 771–780.

Instagram Account: Diana Rice and Anti-Diet Kids. https://www.instagram.com/anti.diet.kids/

STEP 4

Don't Make Them Eat Anything: Build Self-Regulation Skills

"Eat your protein!!"

~ Ava and Kyla's imitation of their nutritionist
mom, not staying in her own lane

Steps 1 and 3 discussed avoiding dieting and a sense of deprivation. Conversely, we have to be careful about encouraging eating. Doing so is the flip side of the same coin and disturbs our children's sense of appetite and self-regulation. Step 4 is about helping our children develop self-regulation skills, the cornerstone of balanced eating. It's surprising to most parents that this Step encourages a more hands-off, less "eat your veggies" approach.

All that said, I want to put in a caveat here. There are indeed times, like when there is a child or young adolescent who is being treated for anorexia nervosa with Family-Based Treatment (FBT) when the parents or caregivers do indeed take responsibility for what their child or teen is eating. If you have a child who is starving, and the plan to keep them out of a hospital-based feeding program is to practice FBT, then the parents may be intimately involved in portioning food, plating food, and ensuring that the child completes meals. Sometimes it's medically necessary to put a child's growth and development first, and the child's responsibility around feeding themselves is taken away or augmented.

However, when growth and development are not at stake in most cases, it's best to follow Ellyn Satter's "division of responsibility," introduced during the last Step and widely tested since 1990. Parents/caregivers are responsible for what, when, and where to eat, and children are responsible for how much and whether to eat. We don't coerce, force, or otherwise dance wildly in the kitchen to encourage our children to eat their vegetables. We don't tell them they can't eat dessert if they don't eat dinner. We don't have a "clean plate club." We don't make food a reward for using the potty or not slugging their brother. Time with an adult that includes food can be a treat or reward, but I discourage you from making *just* the food the prize, or those foods may become "special" for that kid and eaten frantically out of context.

In this Step, we encourage an internal connection around food versus using external messages to decide what to eat. What does this look like? Instead of having a rigid eating schedule, internally driven eating involves listening to hunger and fullness—and eating meals and snacks to match those sensations—most of the time. It means encouraging a peaceful environment where kids taste their food (and notice their body sensations of hunger and fullness) versus having many tasks and distractions during eating. It means that children listen to their bodies—not their parents' or another person's advice—about what to eat and how much of it once the food is on the table.

As a parent and an eating-disorders therapist, I can confidently tell you that this is the best way to feed children. There is science and lots of lived experience behind it. At the same time, staying in our lanes around food is tricky. Why? Because providing for our children's basic needs is one of the main ways we show love and care. When parenting teens, being able to make my daughters a sandwich that they stuffed in their backpacks was very pleasing to me when they were waking, dressing, and driving themselves to school. I could hold on to a little of my mama status in that food-love gesture. That said, I try very hard (and get it right only some of the time, my daughters will attest) not to tell them what to eat or how much of it to eat. They need to develop agency over what they put in their mouths, even though I'm ensuring that the house (and backpack) has some balanced nutrition.

I encourage you to eliminate "good" and "bad" food labels around children and teens. This is something I have really struggled with over my years of practice as a nutrition therapist. There's no good way to categorize food without a moralistic feel. I even cringe a bit at the idea of calling dinner "growing food" and dessert "extra food" because this can confuse some children, too. It's better to have the dessert and the meal on the table simultaneously (yes, I said that), so desserts become less "charged" and look less like rewards and treats than part of a way to eat a well-rounded variety of different foods. You know your kid best, but you'd be surprised how often this rather strange-sounding suggestion neutralizes dessert-type foods if done young enough and before those foods become "charged" and special.

If you try this and end up with the worst-case scenario, where your kid repeatedly eats dessert only and not dinner foods, setting some consistent-among-siblings limits around eating more variety at the meal makes sense. Again, what you decide is less important than the consistency and matter-of-factness of the guideline. One example might be, "We're going to all try some of three different foods before we take out the cookies tonight, so that we're learning to like lots of different kinds of foods." Remember that balanced nourishment happens over days, weeks, and months. One or two or three sketchily eaten meals is not harmful for most growing children in developed countries.

Sometimes it's helpful to talk to kids about hunger and fullness. (You must practice at this yourself to speak about it.) Asking children how they experience hunger so that they understand their own physiological signals can illuminate and open up a dialogue that encourages listening to one's body. Ask them how their thoughts and body change when they feel hungry. For example, when I'm hungry, I experience a churning sensation in my solar plexus (upper gastrointestinal area). If I get over-hungry, I feel spacey and out of focus. Your child's experience of hunger is unique. Why not be curious about it so that she can be, too?

Sometimes it's helpful to distinguish between mouth (or eye) and stomach hunger: when you look at that yummy cake and your mouth wants another piece, but your stomach is full from dinner and doesn't. Tell your child it's okay to eat because of mouth hunger but that eating from stomach-plus-mouth hunger generally feels better in the long run. Don't just assert this. Ask your kids if they remember times when they ate out of mouth hunger and it didn't feel so good. Be curious about their experiences as you share your own. It's always more instructive to ask questions than tell a child what to do—particularly as children get older and want more agency and control over their lives and environments.

It can be helpful to talk about how media sometimes makes us feel hungry, for example, in ads for scrumptious, juicy-looking food or through the power of suggestion. A craving for something can occur because of the suggestion of a sensory delight. At the same time, ads for dieting and diet products can use guilt or shame through photos of thin bodies to make people feel bad about their body size or shape and buy their products. Media literacy goes a long way toward helping kids identify the forces other than hunger, full bellies, or a desire for sensory pleasure that encourage people to say yes or no to food.

Sometimes it's helpful to teach kids that cravings occur when food needs are unmet. We become focused on what is needed when it is denied. This happens with sleep, affection, air, warmth, and food, among other core needs as humans. Concentrating or thinking about anything else can be challenging when you aren't getting enough food. Until that need is satisfied, the craving can be very uncomfortable, and you might become irritable ("hangry") and self-centered. It can be hard to consider other people's feelings. Then, when the hunger is finally met, more than a typical amount of food might be needed to satisfy the craving when it has gone missing for so long. This explains "rebound overeating" that happens after long-term restriction or dieting.

It also explains why some kids turn to food when other emotional needs aren't met. Food can be a stand-in for different types of care and attention. If you watch a child eat compulsively, you might see the food being used for soothing, comfort, company, or grounding. If you suspect this to be true for your child, see if you can offer some alternatives that may provide for those needs. Sometimes just a small amount of connection, attention, touch, listening—and sometimes learning about self-care practices like meditation or journaling—can go a long way toward preventing what could become a habit of emotionally soothing with food nearly all the time.

Of course, there is nothing wrong with eating emotionally. We all do it at times. When it becomes harmful to the body and mind, it typically happens in excess and at the expense of developing more effective and direct coping strategies to meet human needs outside of hunger. There are many different appetites besides food, but knowing which one needs to be fed at any given moment can be confusing.

Consider family-style eating when your children are old enough to serve themselves instead of plating meals for them.

Let them decide what portions feel right through trial and error. Trust them to learn how to do that as they have learned how to do other bodily oriented skills like walking, toileting, and sleeping independently. Yes, sometimes it's bumpy, but eventually they will get it. And it will be smoother if the adults around them don't interfere.

Easier said than done.

So now I have a confession to make. After working in the field of disordered eating for almost thirty years, I still made a grave mistake one morning with my own teenagers. I drove into their lane and told them how and what to eat instead of letting them self-regulate. It was not my proudest parent/nutrition-therapist moment when I said, "I didn't buy avocados so they could get dumped in the compost," one day when my daughters had no stomach for breakfast. One was recovering from Covid and still had an off sense of taste, so food could sometimes be nauseating and not pleasing. I know I was being an anxious mom when I pushed food on her. I also worried about my other daughter, who had ultimate frisbee practice later in the day. I told her that not having a good breakfast might harm her muscles.

This may be true, but I know the golden rule about parenting teens. Telling them what to do—especially about things they are meant to be responsible for themselves (like choosing what and how to eat)—will backfire.

Royally.

Now, if I had a teen with an eating disorder who was teetering on the brink of hospitalization or starving when they should be growing, it would be good limit-setting for me to tell her/

him/them that social or sports participation will be limited if they don't eat a good meal. In this case, I could be saving a life. In practice, I encourage parents to enforce no social or athletic time if food isn't eaten in the case of a chronically under-eating teen. I also think telling my daughter she could be five minutes late for school to eat her breakfast was okay. Priorities.

However, that morning, I crossed a line when my twin daughters (they love to gang up on me) started blaming me for being late for school. (This was back when I was still the driver.) I was up early so I could shower before the morning drive. I made them their favorite avocado toast and bacon, so I was upset when they didn't eat it. I felt that rejection of mama-food-love that I wish I didn't take so personally. I reminded them that I'm not an alarm clock, and they need to clearly tell me if they want a morning nudge at a particular time. And, despite my nudging, they are ultimately responsible for getting up on time for school at age 16.

Furthermore, it wasn't acceptable—to me—for them to leave the house without breakfast. Just because "everyone skips breakfast" doesn't make it right. And that's when I crossed the line and inserted, "I don't buy avocados at your request so that they'll be dumped in the compost."

I started to get resentful and take it personally that my teens were not eating the breakfast I got up early to make and the ripe avocados our family was privileged to afford. I was way over into their lane, trying to regulate their food intake and creating a power struggle around it. Yes, some kids don't have a choice and can't throw any food away because food is scarce in their house, but that was not the case in mine.

My anxiety about them eating well was present because I was projecting the characteristics of my clients onto my non-eating-disordered kids. I was also being a very typically concerned mom. I realized I was overbearing and pushy with food when my daughter needed to complete the power struggle. She refused the avocado toast with bacon, her favorite, even though I brought it into the car. She needed to learn that skipping breakfast doesn't feel good without my intervention. In fact, she did. She used the word "hangry" later when discussing her day.

Every time we tell our kids what to eat or coerce them into eating something in particular (veggies before dessert, more of this, less of that), we override their innate capacity to make decisions about food and learn to self-regulate. We tell them someone outside their body knows better than they do about what to eat, which is—as my teens eloquently would put it—bullshit. As parents, we must step back, make diverse foods available, and let our kids learn to listen to their bodies. This gives them the lifelong skill of knowing how to eat in a balanced, healthful way—incorporating pleasure from food as well as nourishment. I have strived to do this, and my daughters are good, attuned eaters who enjoy a variety of foods most of the time. I don't need to muck this up.

But I'm here to say, with so much empathy, that this is *not* an easy job for a parent. It's hard when you know some things about nutrition and want them to eat a diverse diet. It's hard when one of your kids has some weight loss after a severe illness, and you are worried about her brain development. It's hard when you have an athlete who may not be eating enough to fuel their sport. Yes, it's hard to let go of that time when your kids needed you so much more for feeding—even if the high chair is ancient history.

If you have a child who is not thriving or restricting food during a crucial growth period like adolescence, please seek medical, psychological, and nutritional help, ideally from professionals who have expertise in treating and preventing eating disorders, and operate from a Health-at-Every-Size (HAES) and non-body-shaming perspective. (I wish I could say that these professionals are easy to find. They tend to have full practices because they are in demand.)

Eating disorders are serious mental illnesses, and we must take them seriously. I feel sad when I encounter so many adults who have suffered for decades because their food and body-image challenges were not noticed or treated.

However, other than these more extreme cases, we parents should leave well enough alone and let our kids learn to nourish themselves well by experience. Please encourage them to trust their bodies' hunger and fullness instead of listening to what the social media influencers or other well-meaning others say about eating. No one knows your kids' bodies better than they do.

It humbles me to notice that I quickly fell into the same trap when I felt stressed and vulnerable as a parent that morning of the avocado toast. If I can make this error with all my training in adolescent nutrition and mental health, you might do it, too. As always, I invite you to approach your parenting with self-compassion and let go of perfectionism. We are all doing our best. If you are reading this, there is a good chance you are doing more than most to help your children build healthy relationships with food and their bodies. Standing back and saying less is hard, but allowing our children and teens to build essential appetite-regulation skills is critical.

After school that day, my daughters came home and made themselves an almost identical meal, complete with avocado toast. I'm not making this up. They got the message that mom cares, and they dealt with the "hangry" that came with meal-skipping. They asked if we could get an earlier start the next day so they'd have more time for breakfast. They learned it didn't feel good to miss the breakfast their bodies are accustomed to and need. We all know that prying teens out of bed in the morning is a challenge, and we planned to do our imperfect best with that.

I've tried to remember to let my teenage daughters decide how much of their breakfast to eat—whether they make it or I do. I had only a short time with them before they planned to go to college. All bets are off then, and they'll have to manage their own time and figure out how to feed themselves well. Making us all breakfast is something that I could still do at times. But the caregiving needs to stop there. I'll let them decide how much of that meal to eat. I'll resist the urge to lecture or encourage eating and instead back off and let them self-regulate. Maybe someday, when they have a good adult relationship with food and trust their bodies, they will thank me.

I also know that figuring out how to feed children and teens is not always intuitive. We don't get a manual that says to serve these kinds of foods in these quantities at these ages.

Some of my colleagues in pediatric nutrition have done a great job of creating a blueprint for developmental feeding, letting parents know how much of each food group promotes balanced nutrition and growth for each developmental stage. Even these guidelines (resources are listed at the end of this chapter) should be taken with salt grains, as all kids grow and develop differently.

Picky Eating

What do you do if you have a picky eater? First, know that most kids are fussy at times and go through food jags (eating only white foods, wanting mac-and-cheese for every meal, etc.). While it's maddening when we've cooked a meal with love and care, and a child refuses it, the child is rarely trying to be a pain in the neck. The child often finds a texture or taste foreign and unpleasant, needing more exposure and time to accept it. Most food jags and pickiness get grown out of over time, especially if parents don't get too involved and a power struggle doesn't become part of the mix.

Pediatric nutritionists recommend exposing toddlers to a variety of foods often and early. Giving young ones the ability to eat with their two hands as they develop feeding skills also encourages independence and prevents picky eating. As children grow, please don't put them fully in charge of the meal. Instead of asking, "What do you want for dinner?" give them two options. This gives them some choice and a sense of autonomy but not all the control around the food (unless you like chicken nuggets seven nights a week). Keep offering the foods repeatedly, even if your child initially rejects them. Regular exposure to different tastes and flavors expands your child's palate.

If your child refuses a food, it's best not to have much of a reaction (easier said than done, again). Doing a dance, using coercive techniques around food, or having a significant response about food refusal can actually encourage more reluctant eating in an already cautious or sensitive child. It's not giving in to your child to not react. It's letting them have their feelings and preferences while continuing to serve food that works for your whole family.

I encourage my clients who are parents to avoid the trap of becoming a short-order cook who makes three different meals to match the distinct preferences of each family member. Sure, if there is only one vegetarian, having a meatless alternative is helpful and inclusive, but the family should all eat the same meal, ideally. Children will typically not starve or fail to thrive if they don't like their dinner. They make up the food energy (calories) at other meals and eventually learn that, if they are hungry, it serves them to eat something that might not be their favorite.

My client Mary has three young kids with different preferences. She was exhausting herself trying to feed them, her husband, and herself at the same mealtime with several options. We devised a family meal-planning schedule she told me was a "game changer." Every family member got an evening of the week to pick from their favorite meals and make a choice for the family. Then, they'd make a family schedule of dinners based on these choices. (Mom got a night off on "takeout night.") Each family member ate more flexibly and complained less on the nights when it wasn't their preferred choice because they knew it was only a matter of time before their night would come and they'd get to have their favorite meal. Everyone got excited about making the meal calendar each week and serving "their meal" to the rest of the family. The kids were more involved in food preparation and table-setting, mom eliminated the guesswork at the eleventh hour about what to make for dinner after a long day, and everyone felt more flexible and happy with dinners as a whole. I have tried this plan with lots of success with many families with parents who'd burned out from short-order cooking.

When considering child feeding, particularly picky eating, I love the **Responsive Feeding Therapy (RFT)** framework developed by lead authors Katja Rowell, MD; Grace Wong, MSc, RD, CEDRD-S; Jo Cormack, MA, MBACP; and Heidi Moreland, MS, CCC-SLP, BCS-S, CLC. As you can see by all the diverse letters after their names, the developers of these guidelines come from various medical and behavioral-health disciplines and bring a wealth of perspectives to the table.

The RFT approach builds on a body of research from the field of pediatric feeding and other related areas of study, including responsive parenting, humanistic psychology, attachment theory, interpersonal neurobiology, theories of development, self-determination theory, and trauma physiology. That's a lot of excellent science and psychology folks getting together and coming up with cohesive recommendations around how to work with feeding issues in a way that does the least harm.

"Responsive Feeding Therapy (RFT) is an overarching approach to feeding and eating interventions applicable to multiple disciplines and across the lifespan. RFT facilitates the (re)discovery of internal cues, curiosity, and motivation while building skills and confidence. It is flexible, prioritizes the feeding relationship, and respects and develops autonomy." I highly recommend looking at this online white paper about RFT, quoted above, and the references listed for more detailed information: https://responsivefeedingpro.com/about -rft/. Whether or not you care for a picky eater, the principles and values of this framework are worth reading through. Check in with yourself about whether you practice them at home. They might even be worth sharing with a grandparent or daycare provider who may not know these evidence-based and thoroughly tested principles.

ARFID: Avoidant Restrictive Food Intake Disorder

Avoidant Restrictive Food Intake Disorder (ARFID) is characterized by intense picky eating that results in individuals not consuming enough food for their bodies to work properly. In contrast to Anorexia Nervosa (AN), people with ARFID are not worried about their body image or size. According to the American Psychiatric Association, food restriction with ARFID leads to significant weight loss or failure to achieve expected growth, significant nutritional deficiency, dependence on enteral feeding or oral nutrition supplements, and/or marked interference with psychosocial functioning.

It was not until 2013 that ARFID became listed in the Diagnostic and Statistical Manual of Mental Health Disorders (DSM-5), which proposes three primary presentations of ARFID: "fear of aversive consequences, lack of interest in eating, and sensory sensitivity." ARFID encapsulates an array of long-observed eating issues that had not fit into the previously defined eating-disorder categories. I treated clients with ARFID for many years before there was a label. While labels have their limits, it does mean that this problem can now be studied and treated more effectively.

Discussing ARFID and how to approach this eating disorder is beyond the scope of this book. I'm hopeful that if you suspect your child or someone you love has ARFID, you will reach out and seek help for this complex and often-misunderstood problem. Please see the resources at the end of this chapter as a place to start.

In summary, build self-regulation in children and teens by:

- Preparing food but not telling kids how much of it to eat; letting kids decide how much feels right

- Avoiding "good" and "bad" labels for foods; diversity of diet is ultimately healthiest

- Trying family-style eating versus plating food for children as they get old enough to serve themselves

- Remembering that parents/caregivers are responsible for what, when, and where to eat; children are responsible for how much and whether to eat

- Not using food as rewards

- Setting a regular, but not rigid, meal- and snack-eating schedule for children, and trusting the child's hunger and fullness cues over the schedule

- Encouraging a peaceful environment so that food is tasted (and body sensations of hunger and fullness are noticed) versus having lots of tasks and distractions during eating

- Encouraging children to listen to their bodies—not their parents' or another person's advice—about what to eat and how much of it once the food has been placed on the table

Step 4: References and Resources

Satter, E. *Secrets of Feeding a Healthy Family: How to Eat, Raise Good Eaters, How to Cook.* Madison, WI: Kelcy Press, 2008.

Satter, E. *Child of Mine: Feeding with Love and Good Sense.* Boulder, CO: Bull Publishing, 2000.

Castle, J. and Jacobsen, M. *Fearless Feeding: How to Raise Healthy Eaters from High Chair to High School.* Fearless Feeding Press, 2018.

Jill Castle's online resources for parents and caregivers re: child feeding and eating: https://thenourishedchild.com/

Rowell, K. and McGlothlin, J. *Helping Your Child with Extreme Picky Eating: A Step-by-Step Guide for Overcoming Selective Eating, Food Aversions, and Feeding Disorders.* Oakland, CA: New Harbinger Publications, 2015.

Responsive Feeding Therapy (RFT) White Paper: https://responsivefeedingpro.com/about-rft/.

Menzel, J. "Avoidant/restrictive food-intake disorder: assessment and treatment." In L.K. Anderson, S.B. Murray, and W.H. Kaye (Eds.), *Clinical Handbook of Complex and Atypical Eating Disorders.* London: Oxford University Press, 2018, pp. 149–168.

Breiner, C.E., Miller, M.L., and Hormes, J.M. "ARFID parent training protocol: a randomized pilot trial evaluating a brief parent-training program for avoidant/restrictive food-intake disorder." *International Journal of Eating Disorders.* 2021; 54(12).

Castle, J. *The ARFID Guide: How to Get Help When Your Child is Extremely Picky.* Nourished Child Press, 2022. (https://thenourishedchild.com/product/the-arfid-guide-how-to-get-help-when-your-child-is-extremely-picky/)

STEP 5
Nutrition and (More Importantly) Pleasure

"It looks so pretty. How many foods have purple stripes? But you just want to look at it. You don't want to eat it."

~ me, trying a pepino melon on Kyla's Weekly Weird Fruit Vlog

My daughter Kyla and I have a fun tradition that started her senior year of high school during a stressful time when applying for college (times two for twins) was driving our whole house a little bonkers. We started by buying a "weird fruit" at one of the larger local grocery stores. This strange imported produce was not cheap, mind you, but we would buy a different single weird fruit per week and try it. (Ironically, Kyla was once my picky eater. Not anymore.)

She made silly video recordings of us testing the fruit:

- Saying "cheers"

- Capturing our expressions while tasting the odd flavors and textures

- Rating the experience on a scale of 1 to 10

The pepino melon was gorgeous but tasteless. The dragon fruit looked exotic but didn't deliver as much in the taste department. We loved the kiwano horned melon and thought it tasted like a cross between a kiwi and cucumber.

As a nutrition therapist and foodie, I appreciated this activity as a way to bring a little food-oriented fun into our hectic lives. We laughed a lot, and I enjoyed how she wrote "weird fruit" every week on the family grocery list. Bonding over this vlog was an excellent way to connect during a busy time of life. She told me we'd need to keep the tradition up when she's in college, video-calling each other. I suspect that will be hard to do, and at some point, we'll run out of weird fruit to try. Regardless, the lightness and levity the activity gave to homework- and college-application-filled evenings was priceless.

Step 5 is about balancing nutrition and pleasure and why pleasure is more important than we might think when having a good relationship with food and our bodies. This fruit fun with Kyla reminded me of how I used to make the food on her and her sister's plates look like silly faces when they were little or when we baked together and made a big mess out of the kitchen. Making food preparation and eating fun and light is great for kids and adults alike, especially when so many messages about morality and health are attached to eating.

We can forget that food is a sensory experience meant to be a pleasure and a joy, as well as a way to nourish our bodies and minds. In this Step, we'll look at why focusing on *self-care* when making food choices—instead of *self-control*—is the answer to eating in a way that supports a healthy relationship with our bodies and whole selves.

The health and nutrition fields provide us with so much contradictory information that it can be hard to know how to feed ourselves and our children well. One year's health-food hero becomes another year's health-food monster. (If you are old enough to remember, butter and margarine were classically embroiled in this controversy.) Variety and moderation are not very sexy. They don't sell health books, pills, or plans but are still the gold standard for food and health. Moderation means that there aren't good and bad foods. It means that diversity in the diet is most health-giving. Sharing food is one form of love; all foods can be lovable.

We're going to chat a little more about the nitty-gritty of food procurement, preparation, and nutrition here, but keep in mind that this is not the most critical piece when it comes to encouraging your children to have a healthy relationship with food and their bodies. All of the steps in this book are not meant to be linear. You may continue to revisit Steps 1 through 4, again and again, to remind yourself of the important challenges of body acceptance, staying in your own lane, and intuitive, non-diet-oriented eating.

Before we discuss feeding kids, I want to be clear that the way children eat doesn't always line up with what we adults eat or expect. **Children eat as they grow, sometimes somewhat**

erratically. They may have meals or whole days where they eat more or less than usual. Many parents I've talked to worry that their child is eating in an unbalanced way. Our diet-oriented culture makes us think that, to be healthy, we have to eat perfectly proportioned, colorful meals all the time. This couldn't be further from the truth. Balance happens over days, weeks, and months.

Studies have shown that, left to their own devices, kids typically eat a well-balanced diet without any encouragement from grown-ups. It can be hard to sit back and trust our kids to find their way with food, and there are so many messages about how to eat healthfully out there. Trusting that your child is hard-wired to eat well over time is hard. For most kids, this hard-wiring toward balance is there—at least until the adults start to comment or show emotion about certain food types, introducing imbalance or even confusion.

If you notice that your child always cleans their plate, asks for more, and asks for lots of extra snacks and desserts, there is a good chance that their bodies are hungry and looking for additional calories for growth and development. You may see their growth in spurts, and their eating will match this. Also, sometimes kids don't eat much at school because they focus on academics and socializing; then, they come home ravenous. Don't limit their snacking or worry about this strong appetite. **If children know that food is available when they're hungry, they will start to develop a mindset of abundance and balance around food. If they believe they can't snack or that food is scarce when they feel hungry, they will likely develop a deprivation mindset, which can be the initial catalyst for a challenging relationship with food.**

Ellyn Satter discusses creating "competent eaters" who enjoy food and eating. These young people are comfortable with their enjoyment of food. Competent eaters feel they can eat food they like in satisfying amounts. Eating competence involves *permission* and *discipline*. "Permission to eat food you enjoy in amounts you find satisfying, and the discipline to feed yourself regularly and reliably and pay attention while you eat." This discipline is not the same "willpower" dieters talk about; it's more like developing an attitude of food as self-care, learning that food will be reliably present at regular intervals, so there is no need to hoard or eat beyond needs or comfort.

Letting your child have unrestricted access to desserts and snacks and letting them eat as much as they want at one time flies in the face of what our health- and diet-obsessed culture tells us is correct. However, I'm sure you see your child get tired of new toys eventually. The same is true with food. Your child might be eating a lot of one favorite food when it's still a newly discovered treasure. Eventually, the food will get a little less exciting. If you take the food away or set limits on it, then this does not allow a child to learn to set their own limits on the food. We want to encourage our children to trust in their bodies and appetites. If you don't treat the food as neutral, they may also not treat it as neutral. It's likely to become "charged" in the power struggle; craving and confusion can result.

All this said, while not limiting access to preferred food, some structure around eating can and is helpful for children. Having a loose schedule—regular but not rigid—around meals and snacks is very grounding and essential. It helps kids learn that if they don't eat enough this time, whether it's because they didn't like the food choice offered or because it was more interesting to play with something than to stop for a snack, more food will be available soon. This predictability of meals and snacks provides a sense of abundance and enough-ness that keeps food from becoming an anxious or overly charged event.

In Step 4, I talked about my client Mary, who has a family-meal schedule where each sibling and parent gets to pick one dinner per week. This plan keeps her from being a short-order cook, making three different meals for all the family members' preferences, and includes the family in meal planning and preparation. I learned from my daughters' preschool teachers that kids really like predictability and routine with food. Knowing that Monday is soup night and Tuesday is pasta night is helpful, even if the soup and pasta are changed weekly.

While children's preferences and appetites can be variable—and, again, I don't recommend much encouragement of food with kids—it does help to present regular, balanced meals so that kids learn what balanced, healthful meals resemble. My rule of thumb is to have the five elements present at most meals— and at least a couple of the elements in most snacks.

These include:

1. grain/carbohydrate

2. protein

3. fat

4. produce

5. pleasure

Grains include breads, pasta, rice, quinoa, oatmeal, cereals, and potatoes. Proteins include meat, fish, cheese, yogurt, legumes/beans, eggs, tofu, and other soy-based foods. Vegetarians eat plant-based proteins and must eat roughly three times more plant versus animal sources to get the same amount of protein. Fats include oils, butter, nut butters, cheese, and avocadoes. Produce is fruits and vegetables, notoriously the most challenging for children (often due to texture and freshness factors).

Kyla has always loved fruit, but she would not have touched the strange textures in the weird fruit that she vlogs about today. Her twin sister, Ava, to this day, still doesn't like much fruit unless it's dried, which is vastly different from her fruit-loving, fruit-vlogging sister. In fact, Ava doesn't much like sweet foods in general. She'd rather munch something salty for a snack. These are preference differences, and they should be respected. Again, don't sweat it if your child doesn't eat these mostly water-content fruits and vegetables all the time. They have vitamins and minerals but are not the most caloric, growth-oriented foods. Trust that your child's body needs more calorically dense and nutritious foods if that's what they gravitate towards during a given growth period.

A meal that contains noodles, chicken, and vegetables fits this formula. So does a grilled cheese sandwich with tomato soup or a plate of rice, tofu, and vegetables stir-fried in oil. A ham sandwich with a bunch of grapes or scrambled eggs with toast and fruit also makes a balanced meal. Most snacks contain some of these elements, but not necessarily all of them, and in smaller amounts. It's still best to let your children decide how much they are hungry for and offer something like carbohydrate and protein food at snack time, allowing them to choose how much to eat.

I like to include protein and/or fat with most snacks, as this helps with satiety and prevents those crashes that can happen an hour after eating a not-so-substantial, carbohydrate-only snack. At best, an apple may hold us for only an hour, but an apple dipped in peanut butter or with cheese cubes will be far more satisfying and give your child (and your adult self) far more sustainable energy.

There is no need to teach young children about nutrition. Yes, I'm serious about this. I am, first and foremost, trained as a nutritionist and still feel this way! If there is genuine interest, kids have plenty of time to learn about nutrition later. Concepts like proteins, carbohydrates, and vitamins are typically too abstract for kids. And even curious, science-minded kids don't need a lot of instruction around feeding themselves at a young age. **We want children to connect to the sensory aspects of eating, helping them be in their bodies, noticing their appetites, preferences, and body responses to the food, rather than having an intellectualized approach to eating.** Please read this sentence in bold again. I can't stress it enough.

One of my clients reported that her son's friend, age 6, called strawberries and cream "so bad for me." While some of their social circle called this child's mom "healthy," I don't find this a healthy attitude for a six-year-old to pick up. Strawberries are a vitamin-C-containing, health-enhancing food, and cream provides fat (important for developing brains) and balance for the acid in the strawberries. Furthermore, strawberries and cream are one of the most delicious Springtime treats. My daughters' school used to serve this to the whole student and parent body on May Day. Thinking of a little one considering this "bad" food broke my heart. He could only have learned that from a (perhaps well-meaning) adult who had some fear instilled in her via diet culture.

The fifth important element in a meal or snack is *pleasure*. The meal or snack should be enjoyable. It doesn't have to be the best meal ever for the child to have a positive experience of feeding themselves well. Show your kids that food is fun— and just one of life's many pleasures—by eating food you love with them. Create meals and snacks, ideally together, that are colorful and interesting to eat. Get feedback from your children about what they like and what they'd like you to pack in their lunch; this way, they'll be more likely to eat it and nourish themselves well during their school day. A little attention to preferences can make children more open to other foods that may not be preferred. This creates neutrality around food, not scarcity or limits that tend to make some foods more special than others.

What works for one family regarding meal and snack schedules and content may not work for another. The most important thing is that you work together as a family to find a way to prioritize this primary need that we all have to eat roughly every three to five hours per day. Teach your children that food is vital, but don't make it anxiously approached. Try one system for grocery shopping, meal planning, and eating together as a family. If it doesn't work, try another. Lifestyles change and morph as children grow and families change their schedules. The most important thing is not how many meals you eat together as a family; it's the effort communicated about that desire to spend time together and care for each other with food.

If you need more information about baby weaning or what appropriate amounts of food look like at each child's developmental stage of feeding, I've included some resources at the end of this Step. I want you to know that I—and many other parents—have not consulted such resources when our children were little. Our children grew just fine, using their appetites and some adult guidance around healthy balanced choices. However, if you need direction, reassurance, and more ideas for meals and snacks, my colleagues in pediatric nutrition will provide that for you.

All that said, there is some compelling research about the benefit of family meals. Children who sit down to meals with their families have better mental health, self-esteem, academic performance, resilience, reduced risk of dieting behaviors, reduced risk of developing eating disorders, reduced risk of teen pregnancy and substance use, and improved markers for physical health like cardiovascular health in the teen years. That's incredible! I don't know another nutrition-related habit that has benefits like this. Some of these benefits extend to the adults who participate in the meals, as adults also have decreased rates of depression when they engage in family meals. The most important part of family meal time is the connection and time together.

All of this said, I know it can be amazingly tough to orchestrate family meals when parents and children have opposing schedules and activities. Single-parenting and long work hours are two reasons that little time or energy can be left to plan or prepare meals for a family. Older teens often juggle part-time jobs, homework, and sports, so their appearance at mealtimes can be short and not always sweet. Some families don't have the resources—money and time—to prepare and sit down to eat balanced family meals. And if you live alone some or part of the time—as is true in divorced families—it can be hard to get motivated to make meals for yourself or prepare meals for the days when the kids are there. Life can be downright tiring sometimes, and I have a lot of compassion and lived experience around this.

It's imperative to be flexible and compassionate with yourself around the recommendation I'm making here to embrace family meals. Doing so should not add stress or pressure but provide time for families to connect and place value on sharing food. Takeout or frozen prepared foods are a godsend for many busy families. Also, if you are a mom who identifies as a woman, it does not make you any less of a mom or woman if you do not like to cook. I often say this to clients who feel incredibly guilty that they don't want to spend time and energy shopping and cooking for their families. Again, the critical part of family meals is being together, not the food preparation that goes into that meal. Shopping and cooking can be shared or delegated to others.

While sometimes costly, online grocery delivery and meal services can save some families tons of time and energy. There is no shame in getting a little help from grandma, who loves to cook, or enjoying Trader Joe's popular frozen entrees. Bagged salad can be the easiest way to get vegetables onto a busy table. Not everyone has time to grow their own vegetables or wants to. Some families have to take advantage of food assistance to put food on the table. Know what's possible and important to you around food preparation and provision, and then give yourself some significant grace.

We've often had to eat late at my house because of sports practice or after-school jobs. As a parent providing food, I make sure I have a snack or mini-meal at 5:30, when I start to get hungry, taking care of myself before I take care of the teens coming home late. I like to prioritize eating dinner together whenever I can, even if it means that we eat at 8 p.m. Sometimes I have a meeting, or my partner has a rehearsal, and we all can't eat together. I try to make something that can stay warm on the stove and be self-served, or we have a make-dinner-for-yourself night (not a bad thing for teens to practice before leaving the nest). Sometimes we order takeout on those nights when we can't all eat dinner at the same time together. Again, family meals are about intention and not perfection.

I am well aware that some households don't have the resources—whether time, finances, energy, or desire to cook—and there might be a struggle to prepare meals and teach those essential life skills around food preparation and regular nutrition. Many of my clients feel lost about feeding themselves well because they didn't learn these skills at home or school. Mealtimes were inconsistent, and they often fended for themselves around food with little direction or abundance in their pantries.

I will repeat that the most critical part of family meals is being together, not the food. *(Yes, I'm a dietitian/nutritionist, and I'm saying this.)* The nourishment does not have to be perfect, beautiful, or organic. It's great if you have the time and resources for this and it's consistent with your values, but the most crucial thing about meals for children is consistency and feeling cared for in the process of eating. If children grow up being cared for with food, they will more likely care for themselves that way when they are old enough to do so. If food is interesting but not taking a front seat to the conversation, then food is more likely to have a neutral place and take a back seat to relationships in your children's eventual adult lives. Eating disorders create self-absorption and put a strain on relationships. (I know this because I recovered from one and have worked with those in recovery for decades.) When food and the body become a distraction and a focus over connecting to the ones we love, it's a very lonely place.

Don't fuss so much about the food at the expense of connecting to those at your table. This also bears repeating. Food is a beautiful sensory experience, but it's part of an experience of pausing, taking a break from our day, and connecting with ourselves and those in our environment. Keep the conversation at the table as free from conflict as possible, so that stress does not get associated with eating. To add to the element of pleasure, allow your little ones to get messy and playful with food. I know it's hard if you are a bit of a neat freak like me, but your young child needs to feel, smell, taste, and sometimes wear food to get comfortable with the different textures and sensory environments that diverse foods provide.

I remember putting a big tarp on the floor between my baby twins' highchairs and letting them go at it with the avocado. Yes, they often needed a bath to get the green stuff out of their hair afterward, but they have both been reasonably comfortable with different foods. I am sure that letting them get food into their mouths with trial, error, and confidence was foundational in their now-comfortable relationship with food.

Parents ask me all the time about desserts and sweets. While I believe in the intuitive eating principle of legalizing all foods, some children need gentle limits. This does not mean that sugar is off-limits or restricted. If you need the review, we covered the dangers of this practice in Steps 1 and 4. However, you would probably not let a child into a candy store and give them free rein to eat everything. You would give them a gentle limit. "You can fill this bag with your favorites," or "You can have two dollars' worth." Some kids need gentle structure around meals and foods on special occasions to encourage balance.

The most important thing is being consistent across siblings and practicing any limits you set yourself. It's unfair if ice cream is limited to a small bowl—and Johnny sees Dad eating a large one. So many of my clients who eat compulsively remember they were allowed fewer cookies than their older brothers, who could eat freely. This left my clients feeling deprived (which made them want cookies more) and like something was wrong with their regular appetites. I'm not a fan of having rules around food, but if there are some limits, they must be consistent and flexible. Otherwise, it can be confusing.

Lastly, I understand that you may be trying to protect Susie by offering her less than Sharon, if Susie is a fat child and Sharon is her thin sister. I know you are trying to protect Susie from the cruelty and discrimination that persons in fat bodies are subjected to in our culture today. Please circle back to Step 1 to remember that food restriction may do more harm than I know you are intending. In the following Steps, we'll talk about other ways to care for and strengthen your child, no matter their size and shape.

In summary:

- Love food, and share that love with your children.

- Create meals and snacks that are pleasurable and fun.

- Remember to make available the five elements of balanced meals: 1) grain/carbohydrate, 2) protein, 3) fat, 4) produce, and 5) pleasure.

- Experiment. Change things up, and find what works for your family.

- Eat as many family meals as you can. As schedules get busier when kids get older, continue to prioritize eating some meals as a family.

- Remember that being together is more important than what you serve.

- When needed, and with caution, set reasonable, gentle limits that the whole family can follow around foods that show evidence of being eaten out of balance.

Step 5: References and Resources

Satter, E. *Secrets of Feeding a Healthy Family: How to Eat, Raise Good Eaters, How to Cook.* Madison, WI: Kelcy Press, 2008.

Satter, E. *Child of Mine: Feeding with Love and Good Sense.* Boulder, CO: Bull Publishing, 2000.

The Ellyn Satter Institute. https://www.ellynsatterinstitute.org/

Sumner, B. and Severson, A. *How to Raise an Intuitive Eater: Raising the Next Generation with Food and Body Confidence.* New York, NY: Saint Martin's Publishing Group, 2022.

Castle, J. and Jacobsen, M. *Fearless Feeding: How to Raise Healthy Eaters from High Chair to High School.* Fearless Feeding Press, 2018.

The Family Dinner Project. https://thefamilydinnerproject.org

Utter, J. *et al.* "Family meals and adolescent emotional well-being: findings from a national study." *Journal of Nutrition Education and Behavior,* 49(1); 2017.

STEP 6
Encourage Conscious, Joyful Movement

"There's no such thing as bad weather—only bad clothing."
~ wise preschool teachers of Kyla and Ava

My daughters were privileged to have attended an alternative preschool that insisted on getting the kids outside for a walk every day—rain or shine. Parents were instructed to have rain boots, rain coats, and even rain pants—plus a full change of clothes—for each child in a special clothing bag. As a parent in the diversely weathered state of Massachusetts, I will say that it was sometimes a pain to keep up with making sure there was a dry pair of socks, pants, and underwear every day in their bags. However, I was delighted that my daughters received a true gift: they are scared of no weather and will go outdoors in all elements. They aren't squeamish about mud. Or rain. They don't complain about the cold New England winters; they just bundle up appropriately. (Occasionally, as teens, they wouldn't wear a coat, but that's developmentally appropriate, it seems.)

I appreciate my daughters' foundational comfort around being active outside. They have a true sense of adventure in the outdoors and in life in general. As young adults, they've tried and enjoyed mountain hiking, snow sports, and walks in the rain. I'm including a discussion of physical activity in this book because so many kids, teens, and adults that I've worked with develop a far more complicated relationship with physical activity and fitness.

I'm intentionally replacing the word "exercise" with "movement" because many of my clients and colleagues feel the term "exercise" has been weaponized and often turned into a "should." "Movement" is a term that doesn't seem to create the same feelings of shame and judgment. I'll also note here that having safe spaces in which to move our bodies benefited my daughters and their classmates greatly. Some children don't have inviting streets to walk on or access to safe places to play. And some children have bodies that don't move in typical ways.

Moving our bodies should be fun and bring a joy-filled connection to body and self. Some kids are natural movers and need a lot of activity. They need encouragement to rest and take care of injuries and soreness that may come from using their bodies a lot, especially while growing. One of my daughters is like this. She used to come home from sports practice proudly showing off her bleeding knees. She and I tend to overdo movement at times, as the energy release is an important self-regulator. Her twin sister and my partner are both more naturally sedentary. While Kyla and I need to be reminded to rest and chill out, Ava and Pasha occasionally need some movement to balance their love of chilling on the couch.

If your child moves slowly and likes restful activities, there is absolutely nothing wrong with this innate less-active preference, despite what the diet-and-fitness industry may say. While some exercise is health-encouraging for all bodies, some kids like intense and competitive sports activities, and some prefer solo pursuits, like swinging on a swing set. Different bodies find different activities joyful. The key to whole-person health, as I see it, is to find activities that are both enjoyable and sustainable. As now young adults, Kyla plays ultimate frisbee and tries not to get concussions diving for the disc, while Ava enjoys what she calls "hot girl power walks" on her way to buy flowers and matcha tea for her friends.

Finding activities to complement your children's various movement personalities can be difficult, especially when needs and preferences are different. That said, finding activities that are pleasurable and fun for kids will go a long way toward creating a healthy relationship with movement and a healthy connection to the body. Moving together as a family sets the foundation for appreciating some of the benefits of an active body, as well as helping kids develop skills around balance, teamwork, pacing one's energy, healthy vs. unhealthy competition, and the list goes on.

I want to say a few words here about ability. Obviously, different bodies are differently abled. Some children are natural athletes, and their bodies are well-coordinated. Some children have physical disabilities and are unable to move in the ways most humans get around in the world, sometimes requiring assistance from other humans and devices to allow that movement. Most children fall somewhere in between these extremes. It's important to honor and respect your child's innate movement style and limitations. This may be hard if you are an athletic parent with a less physically active child—or a disabled parent with a hyperactive child. Awareness, compassion, and open communication can go a long way.

I have heard so many stories from adults who were shamed as children for their natural sedentary or less-coordinated way of moving about in the world. This shame often goes deep and leads to a complicated relationship with the body and physical activity. Shame may encourage some children and adults to feel cut off and disconnected from their bodies. Since the body is where we feel emotions like love, pleasures like comfort, and present-moment focus, it is truly heart-breaking to encounter someone who is cut off from the delights of being in a body because the pain and grief around connecting with the body has been too much. Many of my clients share stories about how challenging it has been for them to be in their bodies because they believed their bodies were wrong or less desirable than others' from a young age.

While many kids and teens learn from adults and the internet that the reason to exercise is to "look better" or to lose weight, there are so many other reasons to encourage physical activity. For many, enjoying physical movement creates a foundation for a healthy, happy life. Studies have documented that overall quality of life is rated significantly higher by those with physically active lifestyles, no matter their age and health status. Large-muscle movements lead to increased strength, stamina, and flexibility into old age. According to the Centers for Disease Control (CDC), physical activity benefits brain health, strengthens bones and muscles, and improves the ability to do everyday activities.

I don't believe that being "active" for most people means going to the gym regularly, though that's fine if you enjoy gyms. My grandparents lived into their 90s without gym workouts or special diets of any kind. I'm sure genetics was on their side, but I think being active and engaged in life must have played a role in their health. Nana, in her late 90s, was literally still kicking when I first wrote this book chapter. Housecleaning (her house was remarkably tidy), cooking, and actively engaging with grandkids were her main sources of "exercise" and they served her well. "If you don't move it, you lose it," she always said.

Fitness may be the most significant factor known for prevention of disease and injury. In fact, while we can't show that weight has a causative factor in health and mortality, there is irrefutable evidence of the effectiveness of regular physical activity in the primary and secondary prevention of several chronic diseases. Strong scientific evidence (albeit conducted decades ago, see references at the end of this chapter) shows that a regular dose of physical activity reduces by about 30% the risk of premature death, cardiovascular disease, stroke, type II diabetes, colon and breast cancer, and depression.

Physical activity improves quality of living by improving sleep and decreasing stress. It may also play an important role in the management of mild-to-moderate mental-health conditions, especially depression and anxiety. Although people with depression tend to be less physically active than non-depressed individuals, increased aerobic exercise or strength-training has been shown to reduce depressive symptoms significantly. The benefits of physical activity on anxiety symptoms and panic disorder seem to equal that of medication or relaxation. (In general, acute anxiety responds better to exercise than chronic anxiety.) Moving our bodies should be fun and not feel like a chore, even if it is literally like medicine. Joy is what makes it sustainable.

Physical fitness is one's ability to execute daily activities with optimal performance, encompassing cardiovascular endurance, muscular strength, flexibility, and balance. Contrary to some beliefs, fitness is available to all body shapes and sizes. **The health benefits of exercise benefit those who are moving in any kind of body.** Fatter people who are fit are significantly healthier than leaner people who are not fit. In fact, research has demonstrated what has been called the "obesity paradox." In one study, "fit, obese men [classified based on the BMI, which we know is not meaningful; see Step 2] had a lower risk of all-cause and cardiovascular mortality than unfit, lean men." Another study showed in patients with established cardiovascular disease and other chronic conditions (kidney disease, severe arthritis) that those in the "overweight" and "obesity" classifications had a better prognosis than lean patients. The Health at Every Size (HAES) ™ movement has been born partly from the significant research that shows that fatter people who are fit are significantly healthier than leaner people who are not fit.

People who are physically active report higher self-esteem and fewer negative feelings related to body image than those who are less physically active. Physical potential can boost confidence and can encourage an appreciation for the body for reasons other than appearance. Because computers and social media are so captivating for our kids and keep them in one place for many more hours than past generations, it's particularly important that we encourage physical activity for balance and teach kids about the social, emotional, and health benefits of moving. At the same time, please remember my discussion in the first chapter about shame and the negative effects it has on health. **Shaming our children into moving their bodies may cancel out those health benefits of the physical activity.**

It's also important not to tell children you are exercising to lose weight or to make up for what you ate the day before. This is *not* the best motivation for exercise. Instead of saying, "I had too much ice cream last night, and I need to go to the gym," consider saying, "I had so much fun at my Zumba class. Will you dance with me in the kitchen to my favorite song from class?" or "I'm really looking forward to jumping in the pool. My body feels so good after a swim." Healthy habits can be encouraged for the whole family, and they should not be about changing your child's or your weight. **When physical activity gets tied to weight loss or compensating for food eaten, it creates a more compulsive and disordered relationship to fitness.** Moving for the sake of pure joy and feeling good is more sustainable, and it allows for rest, too, when the body needs relaxation more on any given day.

In my first book, *Nourish*, I discuss the concept of mindful, conscious, joyful movement. I make a clear distinction
between the type of exercise regimen that the Fitbits of the
world prescribe and the kind of activity that we engage in
because our bodies and minds desire and ask to move. In fact,
if you are walking just to get a thumbs-up from your handheld
device, then that is probably going to get old fast. It's going to
get really old if you are a child or teen moving only to "please"
a parent or coach. True love of physical activity comes from
being *in* the body, feeling the air on your skin, the strength
of your muscles, the rhythm of breathing. It does not come
from checking off boxes or pleasing another person or device.

If you are counting calories or trying to please a trainer,
you might not be in your body truly experiencing the joy of
moving. You might also not notice an injury in the quest to
meet an external goal. Fitness goals aren't inherently bad, but
they should never be a substitute for operating from within
the body. Physical activity is truly about being in your body
(ideally, getting a break from being in your mind) and being
in the present. If the workout feels good and is fun and engaging, you'll be more likely to do it again and again. Maybe for
decades. If the exercise is tedious, exhausting, punishing, or
completely attached to an external prescription (steps, calories,
etc.), then it is less likely to be aligned with what your body
wants at that very moment. The movement might be boring,
stressful to the body, or compulsive.

In my experience, people who maintain regular physical
activity throughout their lives do so because they drop joy-
fully into the present moment in ways that feel good. If they

wake up one morning and feel tired, they allow themselves a day off to sleep in and rest their muscles. If they are injured, they modify their exercise—or ask a physical therapist to help them with recovery. They get the benefits of exercise because they are not creating excess stress in the body system; they are doing something that feels nourishing. Adults often have to find this joy of movement themselves in order to instill it in their children.

While physical activity is great for the body and mind, even too much of a good thing can be harmful. Many of my clients exercise compulsively. They can't take a day off without tremendous guilt and self-flagellation. When I dig deeper, they often don't really like the exercise they are doing. Running hurts their knees, or yoga makes them feel incompetent around all the young pretzel-types. Somewhere they got into their heads how much exercise they needed to do in a week. They stick to it religiously. That's fine if it lines up with what feels good in their bodies and their life falls nicely into place around that schedule, but so often I hear about hours of sleep lost, social engagements declined, and injuries worsened because the workout program was literally in charge. The joy of moving the body gets stripped from the activity when it becomes compulsive.

It's wonderful to encourage movement in your children, but not too much or at the exception of other meaningful life pursuits. Please also take into account personal temperament around physical activity. If you yourself feel wrong when you don't run six miles, but, then, after you do those miles, you are completely wiped out and exhausted the rest of the day, that's a red flag. Your relationship with exercise could be off. Listen and respect your body's wisdom about how much activity is right or enough for you on a given day—and teach your children the same.

Here are some questions to ask when you are trying to find movement that is joyful for yourself or your family:

- What form of movement nourishes and feels good to your body and soul?

- Do you like to move outside or inside—or a combination of both? Is this weather dependent?

- Do you like to move your body alone or with others?

- Do you have more energy for physical activity in the morning, afternoon, or evening?

- How does movement fit best into the rest of your life?

- Does vigorous or more gentle action ground you? If both do, does it depend on the day?

To cultivate mindful, conscious, joyful movement for you and your family:

- Find ways to move that you love and that help you feel present and accepting of your amazing, unique body.

- This may seem obvious, but don't play sports that you hate. I hear teens in this situation quite a lot. A long-term sustainable healthy attitude about physical movement is more important than forcing an unhappy athlete to continue on the path.

- Listen to your body. If you feel sore, tired, and spent after exercising, you may be doing too much at a level that is not sustainable—or your daily-activities plate may be too full for that level of physical activity.

- Never ignore injuries. Soreness, when you use new muscles, is normal, but pain is a message from your body. What is it trying to tell you? Stop. Rest. Heal.

- Think outside the box (or gym). Find ways to move that feel good in daily life. Take the stairs. Walk the dog. Bike downtown. Stretch when you've been sitting too long on the couch with your laptop doing homework.

It's also very important to see that your children and teens are eating enough food and getting enough rest to sustain and support high levels of activity, especially for those that are in daily dance classes or varsity sports. When I was a young dancer, I really had no idea how much food would support my hours in the studio. I often dieted because I thought that was what I needed to do to have the "ballerina body," but then I couldn't understand why I came home from dance classes in the evening and wanted to eat everything in the house. You may be surprised by just how many calories and how much sleep an athlete needs to repair all the muscle fibers and tissues that break down and build up with regular running, weightlifting, or dancing. If your child or teen is also growing (brains and many organs are, until about 25), then they need even more calories for that critical process. Teens who are athletic can truly eat you out of house and home—and that's normal for the amount of activity and growth they are engaging in at the same time.

If your kids are getting enough food and sleep, and they are not training beyond their bodies' capacities, then they should be able to recover from their physical activities and feel good (albeit a little sore) the next day. If your kids' exercise routine is wiping them out, then it's time to look at their eating and other habits. A sports nutritionist (ideally one who works with adolescents and is trained to screen for disordered eating) can help if your athletic teen needs some education around how to fuel their sport effectively. **Many of my clients are surprised that just adding more food (often carbohydrates) gives them more energy and helps their bodies recover better from physical training.** Under-fueling through under-eating impacts the young body in innumerable ways, affecting the endocrine (hormonal) system as well as the metabolic system. Chronic lack of nutrition is dangerous over time. It affects athletic performance and long-term health.

There is some good evidence that yoga as a movement form can be supportive of a healthy connection to the body and to movement. Yoga, in its purest form, promotes an embodying experience, which is at the heart of having a positive body image and sense of one's self. There are many styles and forms of yoga. Although strengthening and stretching is part of the practice, there are also breathing techniques, meditative exercises, and mindfulness opportunities. These improve one's "capacity to respond adaptively to the dynamic association continuously unfolding between the demands of one's internal (e.g., thoughts, feelings, physiology) and external (e.g., family, community, broader culture) experiential self-systems," says researchers Webb and others in a recent journal article critiquing Westernized yoga. This means yoga may encourage embodiment or embodied awareness.

Embodied awareness is a way for us to connect to the present moment by using the body, the breath, or any other sensory experience to ground ourselves. Yoga encourages this awareness, but the context seems to be important. Embodying experiences are more likely if yoga studios and instructors eliminate mirrors, appearance-orientation, and discussion of weight and shape. Yoga instructors should offer poses that are just challenging enough while remaining safe, comfortable, and inwardly focused, instead of focusing on what and how others are doing the poses. This encourages safety, respect for the body, and an empowering student-teacher relationship. Certain poses such as Warrior I and II also represent agency and functionality, challenging the social constructs of the female gender as submissive, passive, and weak.

Studies of yoga with teens show mixed results as to whether it improves body image. Webb and colleagues again argue that yoga's rapid rise in Western culture since the 1970s has to be understood in terms of the commercialization, appearance-focus, celebrity, and fitness culture. "The yoga body" and the culture surrounding yoga create barriers for people with marginalized social identities like ethnic minorities, higher-weight individuals, people with disabilities, and people with lower socio-economic status. This is not how yoga, inclusive for all, was intended. All bodies deserve embodiment practices. With the right teacher and mindset, yoga designed for kids and teens of all body types can be empowering and foster integration of mind, body, and spirit.

As I said before, my family has four members with very different movement styles. Kyla would choose to hike and snowboard with friends over her school vacation, while Ava says, "not my vacation vibe." She would choose to enjoy lots of snuggly time on the couch reading or watching her favorite Netflix series. They both needed a break from the stress and intensity of exams and college applications and chose to unwind differently. They've always been different that way, though they both seem to find a balance between movement and rest most of the time. My musician partner is more inclined to be chill, while I'm oriented toward regular movement, given my dance background. Despite our different movement temperaments, we often go for walks together. Sometimes I will go swimming while he sits by the water and watches the waves; sometimes he will join me. When we go out to see live music, I could dance all night, while he's more likely to be still and study the other musicians' craft. Sometimes he dances along with me. As a family, we've had to navigate those differences, letting the teens hike the trails out ahead of the slower 50-somethings.

I'll end by sharing that my personal favorite way to "exercise" is to have a dishwashing dance party. At my house, we have a sparkly disco light and a lengthy dance-party playlist.

My family has been known for impromptu kitchen dances. Other joyful family movement might include hide-and-seek (even in the house), hula hoops in the park or yard, and games like Twister. If movement is fun and part of daily life, then it's not a chore, nor is it compulsive and over-stressing. **Movement is like eating; it is a pleasure that sustains us and reminds us that being in a body is one of the joys of life.** Encourage your kids to enjoy a balance of movement and stillness and honor their bodies' wisdom around what feels good.

In summary,

- Avoid shaming around physical activity and appreciate your child's individual style of movement: athletic or differently abled, active or sedentary, and everything in between. Be very careful with young people around judgments of the body at all.

- Do active things together as a family in order to give your child a foundation for sustainable, fun movement and connection to the body.

- Encourage outdoor time as a family, in order to take a break from computers and appreciate the natural world and how it feels to move in it. Leisurely walks in the park do count.

- Teach children and teens about the joyful aspects of physical activity—and eventually the health and mental-health benefits—but don't make exercise about losing weight or making up for food eaten. The latter encourages a more compulsive and disordered relationship with exercise that is more about self-control than self-care—and generally less sustainable.

- Remember that you and your children do not need to work out to have good bodies. This is a myth rooted in ableism, healthism, and many kinds of privilege. Honor the different movement temperaments of your different children in their unique bodies. Let your kids move how they want to or don't want to.

- Consider one of your jobs as being a blockade from what the money-making diet/beauty/fitness culture is trying to shove down your kids' throats everywhere on social media and otherwise. Repeat messages of balance, gentleness, and moderation often.

Step 6: References and Resources

Rejeski, W.J., Mihalko, S.L. "Physical activity and quality of life in older adults." *Journal of Gerontology Series A: Biological Sciences and Medical Sciences.* 2001;2:23–25.

Brown, D.W., Balluz, L.S., Heath, G.W., Moriarty, D.G., Ford, E.S., Giles, W.H., and Mokdad, A.H. "Associations between recommended levels of physical activity and health-related quality of life. Findings from the 2001 Behavioral Risk Factor Surveillance System (BRFSS) survey." *Preventive Medicine.* 2003;37(5):520–528.

Warburton, D.E., Nicol, C.W., and Bredin, S.S. "Health benefits of physical activity: the evidence." *Canadian Medical Association Journal.* 2006;174(6):801–809.

Paluska, S.A. and Schwenk, T.L. "Physical activity and mental health: current concepts." *Sports Medicine.* 2000; 29(3):167–180.

Lee, C.D., Blair S.N., and Jackson, A.S. "Cardiorespiratory fitness, body composition, and all-cause and cardiovascular disease mortality in men." *The American Journal of Clinical Nutrition.* 1999;69(3):373–380.

Lavie, C., De Schutter, A., and Milani, R. "Healthy obese versus unhealthy lean: the obesity paradox." *Nature Reviews Endocrinology.* 2015;11:55–62.

Association for Size Diversity and Health (ASDAH). https://asdah.org/

Liu, M., Wu, L., and Ming, Q. "How does physical-activity intervention improve self-esteem and self-concept in children and adolescents? Evidence from a meta-analysis." PLoS ONE 2015;10(8): e0134804. (https://doi.org/10.1371/journal.pone.0134804)

Schauster, H. *Nourish: How to Heal Your Relationship with Food, Body, and Self.* Somerville, MA: Hummingbird Press, 2018.

McCall, L.M. and Ackerman, K.E. "Endocrine and metabolic repercussions of relative energy deficiency in sport." *Current Opinion in Endocrine and Metabolic Research.* 2019;9:56–65.

Cook-Cottone, C., Cox, A., Neumark-Sztainer, D., and Tylka, T. "Future directions for research on yoga and positive embodiment." *Eating Disorders: The Journal of Treatment and Prevention.* 2020;28(4):542–547.

Webb, J.B., Rogers, C.B., and Thomas, E.V. "Realizing yoga's all-access pass: A social justice critique of westernized yoga and inclusive embodiment." *Eating Disorders: The Journal of Treatment and Prevention.* 2020;28(4):349–375.

Sole-Smith, V. Burnt Toast Newsletter. https://virginiaso lesmith.substack.com/

STEP 7

Discuss Social Media and Build Community: Real Love Is Better than Virtual Like

"You can play with your phone or change
the world. You don't get to do both."

~ Robin Sharma

This quote has been on my fridge since my daughters were about fourteen. They tease me and say that I blame everything on the cell phone. I grew up in the 1970s and was a teen in the 1980s. I didn't have a cell phone until I was in my 30s. In fact, I think the barrage of information and opinion that teens (and younger) take in from the internet and phone are a huge challenge that I feel grateful I never had to navigate.

Kids and teens today not only have to evaluate what their parents, teachers, and other authority figures expound, they have to evaluate the outpouring of celebrities and "influencers" of many types on social media. It's constant because it's all at their fingertips. The moment they are procrastinating doing their homework or bored with their siblings, they enter a world of entertainment. A report released by Common Sense Media in 2015 found that teens (ages 13 to 18) use an average of nine hours of entertainment media per day. Tweens (ages 8 to 12) use an average of six hours per day. These figures are not including time spent using media for school or homework.

Because screen time is so pervasive, it can be hard for adults to be discerning about it, never mind children and teens. I'm writing this book at a computer and I counsel many clients virtually over Zoom, so I absolutely understand the benefits of technology. That said, it's extremely important that both adults and kids learn how to set boundaries around what they ingest from the internet and social media because there is so much out there.

There have always been marketers using ads to target children as future consumers, but now advertising is more embedded and insidious on websites and social-media platforms. When I watch a streamed sporting event, I will often count at least a half dozen forms of "hidden" advertising in each visual frame. We consciously and unconsciously take this branding in. As I mentioned in Step 1, the diet and beauty industry markets to younger and younger people today, making it seem like you aren't okay if you don't do something to change or improve your face or body.

Teens and Body Image

I am going to spend some significant time here on bodies and puberty. I want to encourage you to talk to your kids about puberty before it happens. I don't just mean the birds and the bees, though that's super important. I mean talking to them about the diversity of bodies.

Do this frequently.

Why? Because this kind of discussion will counteract the millions (yep, millions) of images of people that your child or teen will see in videos, advertising, and on social media. The vast majority of these images highlight perfected, filtered, and idealized bodies. Reminding kids of those filters encourages good media literacy. Yes, models and celebrities have pores and cellulite like the rest of us, but they also have their own makeup artists and personal trainers. Also, computers enhance the heck out of their images to make them look "perfect."

Due to media exposure, research has shown that children as young as three or four are able to understand and express social standards and stereotypes related to bodies and weight. Think about children's movies and what the heroes and villains look like. Thinness and fatness are represented with significant stereotypes in most kids' programming. One analysis of ten popular children's shows in 2020 found attractiveness was associated only with thin characters. Kids take this in and don't even realize they are being encouraged to like one body type over another. The Barbie doll, updated only slightly over the decades, has proportions such that, if she were a real woman, she wouldn't be able to stand upright, support her own weight, or menstruate.

These images, which come to us at a young age and continue over our lifetimes, set our preferences. If the images change, so will our preferences. History shows this to be true, as the thin ideal is a more recent preference that has not been presented throughout history. As caregivers, you can be very neutral about bodies with your kids and expose them to diverse body types, but the machine of the media, including social media, is working hard to shape those preferences. Social media includes a high proportion of appearance-related content, including images that promote appearance comparisons selected and edited with the goal of presenting appearance ideals. Again, the lucrative diet and beauty industrial complexes are at the core of this content. If we felt comfortable with how we looked, we wouldn't buy the beauty product or body-improvement program.

Even the fat-acceptance movement on Instagram and TikTok has been called out as a platform that is specifically designed to make people feel worse about themselves. The "fat" content is filtered, staged, and shot to portray an unrealistically happy life and often unrealistic bodies. In addition, there is creepy corporate stalking. Sadly, many people who attempt to access body-acceptance content on social media immediately get bombarded with weight-loss ads.

Beyond increasing awareness around media and corporate motives, please also talk to preteens about how natural it is to have body and weight changes throughout life, especially at puberty. Preteens get round. Yes, that soft, squishy tummy is normal. Adolescence is the time of life, second only to infancy, when the body and brain grow exponentially fast. In the preteen years, the body needs to obtain extra fat weight. That increase in body proportions provides reserves that help fuel important teenage growth and development.

If preteens are allowed to round out naturally, without interference from well-meaning parents or healthcare providers, most of that roundness fuels important tissue and organ growth. Interfering with your child's weight by putting them on a diet or by encouraging unnatural "six-pack" abs may stunt the development of their brain, vital organs, and height, never mind their self-esteem. When teens look at the Instagram profiles of "fit-fluencers," they get an unhealthy sense of how much exercise or muscle is normal for most individuals' bodies and lifestyles.

If you notice your kids dieting because they are dancers or athletes being encouraged to "reduce," do something about that. Reach out to their dance instructor or coach and remind them that performance is about hard work and determination, not body type. Yes, maybe body type matters to an Olympic athlete where a fraction of a second makes a difference in a race, and body proportions matter. (Notice that swimmers and runners tend to have different and somewhat homogenous body types at the elite level.)

However, encouraging a team of young people to lose weight to get faster will likely have the opposite effect for most kids as they deplete their caloric fuel. Those who improve their times when they diet may harm their ability to be sustainable athletes and movers for many decades to come, as tissues get stressed. Running on fumes almost always leads to injuries, illness, and burnout. Don't let coaches prioritize winning if it's at the expense of your child's self-esteem and health.

A popular aesthetic among teen models is to be prepubescent and razor-thin. This prepubescent look is not most bodies. Who says that all bellies can't be beautiful in cropped tops? Our culture does. Even kids who conform to this thinner ideal body type at age 13 might not at age 17. Please talk about body changes at home while your kids are taking in all those images. Challenge them to find pictures on Instagram of humans with diverse body sizes, asymmetrical features, and disabilities. Encourage them to find role models who care for their whole selves and have meaningful lives, not just stereotypically attractive bodies.

My intern Julianna told me about a scary trend on TikTok where celebrities, fitness professionals, and other influencers show videos of what one of their meals look like. She found this "toxic," as do I, because no one meal makes a clear picture of the food intake of any individual. No one sees what that person eats the rest of the day or week. No one sees the more frantic eating of more pleasurable food after the perfect veggie-laden photo shoot. These trends are dangerous because they may encourage teens who are growing to underfeed themselves in imitation or provide pressure to eat in a more orthorexic ("clean") way.

My kids got tired of my bodies-come-in-all-different-sizes rants, but I later heard them repeating similar words to teenaged friends who shared negative body thoughts. They told their friends they love them and they are so much more than their bodies. They heard it so much themselves growing up, and they believe it. (At least some of the time. The cultural messages are strong for everyone, sadly, no matter how much opposition we interject.)

Sometimes it's essential to be a broken record with our children when our culture is so broken and wrapped up in body ideals based on making most people feel shame so they will buy the next diet book, pill, or beauty and fitness product. Furthermore, insidious racism and weight discrimination exist on so many levels. People in larger bodies experience oppression every single day in this culture. Let's not be blind to this oppression around body size, just as we are trying not to be blind to racism in our culture. **Let's work toward change, appreciating bodies of all different shapes, sizes, colors, and abilities, in order to bring more openness and acceptance to future generations.**

If your preteen doesn't freak out about the naturally soft belly that is a hallmark of early puberty, then she/he/they will be less likely to freak out someday about natural middle-aged body shifting, or child-bearing weight changes, or their body softening in a pandemic. Sprinkle body-acceptance messages early and often with kids you spend time with. Tell them that real faces don't have filters; they have pores, blemishes, and scars. Real legs aren't always smooth. Real bellies aren't always flat or muscular. A healthy adult relationship with food, body, and self depends on it.

Body Positivity/Acceptance/Neutrality

I want to say a word or two about body positivity vs. body acceptance vs. body neutrality. There has been a lot of discussion among my therapeutic book-club members—and professionals in my field—about the differences between these terms. Some people in recovery from disordered eating and body-image disturbance feel that **body positivity** (feeling good about one's body) is unattainable. Some people with chronic illnesses that dramatically affect the body and how it functions also feel that a positive outlook on the body is too much to ask. Ultimately, in the work that I do with clients, I aim for **body acceptance and neutrality** over positivity (although if someone can love and feel positive about their body, then that is wonderful). Body neutrality means that you accept and respect your body, even if it isn't the way you'd like it to be. You exist within your body without holding judgment or strong opinions about how it looks.

In a culture that has such narrow parameters for what makes a "good" or "attractive" body, it is important that we don't put too much importance on what the body looks like. Period. Being embodied and operating "inside" the body (rather than being on the outside looking at and judging the body) is something to aim for. Accepting and feeling neutral about the inevitable body changes of aging is something that we can teach our kids at a young age and through our example. **Bodies change, grow, soften, wrinkle, and reflect lifestyles. All bodies are good and acceptable and unique.** And bodies are only one part of the whole self. (More on this in Step 10.)

If you value the whole self as being more expansive and important than the body, then that value can be taught to your children. Our selfie-driven, image-focused culture will certainly compete with you and your valuing of the whole self. However, your children may more critically view the health and wellness gurus who are trying to sell supplements and creams by making them feel badly about their looks. Your kids may be able to resist idealizing the physical images of celebrities or models if physical appearance is just not that important to them.

Research shows us that what we look at shapes what we believe is attractive. **Remind your kids that "attractive" can also include personality, uniqueness, energy, and spirit**. Repeat this one often, since the focus on beauty and image is so pervasive in our wider culture. **Help your kids find role models who have value other than their outer appearance, and encourage them to include those role models in their social media feeds**. It doesn't hurt to clean out your own social-media accounts, eliminating any people that you follow that make you feel bad about yourself or "less than." If you need some ideas, see the end of this chapter for a list of body positive/neutral Instagram accounts and podcasts at the time of this book's publishing. This list will hopefully continue to grow as awareness and interest increases.

Be Proactive in Your School Community

Children and teens spend a lot of time at school. I invite you to make sure that your school community is an inclusive and supportive environment for all bodies. If your school community has some practices that are not inclusive or may promote disordered eating, the Alliance for Eating Disorders has some resources, including form letters, which can be sent to school systems that continue to teach about "good" and "bad" foods or weigh children. Here's that link: https://www.allianceforeatingdisorders.com/resource-library/

The Multi-Service Eating Disorders Association (MEDA) names these Do's and Don'ts around making your school a Body Confident Community.

DO:

- Talk respectfully and kindly to other people—and to yourself

- Focus on others' strengths and qualities other than appearance

- Recognize that we all come in different shapes and sizes; no body type is better than another

- Challenge media images of "perfect" appearance

- Encourage friends to look after and respect their bodies

- Examine your school's library and consider donating books that celebrate body diversity

DON'T:

- Discuss people's weight and appearance

- Talk about "junk food" or "bad" versus "good" foods

- Comment on your own body in a negative way

- Talk about diets or other "quick fixes" to change your body

Build Community to Combat Negative Media Influences

I believe that our children are less likely to be influenced and stigmatized by the celebrities and advertisers on social media if they have a community of people around them—adults and peers—who celebrate their uniqueness and love them for who they are. Parents need supportive peers around them, too, so that they don't get sucked into the latest diet trend or food fad. We may turn to "control strategies" around food when we aren't getting our greater needs met.

Food is representative of care and love to many of us, and when we have deficits in the care and love department in our lives, we can turn to food as a way to care for ourselves or feel more in control. Eating good food is indeed self-care, but it is only one source of self-care. We need care in so many ways. It's good to check in and notice if food (or the control of it) is standing in for deep connection, intimacy, and meaning in our lives. It's easy to slip into that pattern; it's almost socially sanctioned.

Building meaningful connections with peers and caring adults is important for young people. We have to make sure that time on the phone or behind the screen does not take away from reaching out for real human contact and connection. It's also important that we have other adults in our lives who parent with similar values. If you are trying to have a non-diet, Health-at-Every-Size (HAES)™ orientation in your family, it can sometimes be hard to find other families who are doing the same thing. We're all digesting the same messages from the media, so we can second-guess ourselves.

Abigail is a dietitian/nutritionist for whom I provide clinical supervision. She asked me recently if it was okay to feed processed food to her one-year-old. She was feeling guilty because a friend was following a "no processed food" diet for her own baby. Abigail began to feel badly about her own feeding practices. She's a nutrition professional herself, so she started wondering if it was shameful to give a frozen waffle to her child. Her little girl loves waffles, so it seemed like a fun-filled breakfast, but she was beginning to doubt her choice. This mom is someone who has worked in the field of eating disorders and been in recovery from her own, so she embraces intuitive eating and a non-diet, non-restrictive lifestyle around food. Regardless, she felt conflicted.

This example illustrates how even those of us who work in the field of eating disorders and truly believe that there are no "good" or "bad" foods sometimes get sucked into diet culture. We want so much to do the "right" thing by our children that we second-guess our amazing intuition. Those gut feelings about how we should feed and parent our children are important and worth listening to. Parenting is not something that can be learned from a book (and, believe me, I read a lot of them in the early days). **Parenting is as much a feeling as a thinking process.** We need both our guts and our brains to be in gear—which is damn hard when we're sleep-deprived or overworked.

I encouraged Abigail to continue to feed her daughter the waffles that she loves and to not feel bad that she doesn't make them from scratch with all-organic ingredients. As parents, we need to pick our battles and decide where we put our time and energy. In my mind, it's better to get down on the floor with your toddler to play than design the "perfect" meal. If it feels deeply nourishing for you as a parent to make something from scratch, then, by all means, do it—but do have awareness that even the cleanest, organic ingredients have been processed *some way*—unless you are milking the cow and grinding the grain you grew in your own backyard. **The idea that we have to keep our kids away from processed food is not only orthorexic (again, a condition in which the sufferer systematically avoids specific foods in the belief that they are harmful)—it's also nearly impossible.**

I share this story of a well-meaning, doubting mom because I want to highlight the fact that even the most educated professionals who are doing their own work to block perfectionist feeding attitudes may fall prey to it with the comments of a friend, or the stray ad, or the surprising negative body thought. As someone who has recovered from an eating disorder and developed a healthy relationship with food and my body over a few decades, even I have to pause sometimes and remind myself that the latest superfood is not all that. I've had to remind myself that repeatedly encouraging my teens to eat protein at breakfast is disrupting their intuitive eating and likely going to backfire. (It did.) Even those of us who have literally written books on this subject have to karate chop the health messages (often diet messages in disguise) that come into our spheres, allowing our children to trust their own bodies' wisdom as they develop their very own relationships with food and eating.

While parents and direct caregivers are certainly influential in children's lives, other adult community with shared values can go a long way. I know that my daughters appreciate hearing wisdom from their aunts, even if that wisdom is the same thing I've shared in the past. I always talk to my teens about the importance of sleep, but when their pediatrician talked about their need for nine hours per night, they started to get to bed earlier. When a conversation with me is awkward, I know that my daughters can go to any number of my friends or siblings to chat about it. I'm grateful that they have other adults in their lives that care about them and give them perspectives that are sometimes different from that of their parents.

I'm also grateful that my daughters have good friends, many who I care about like they are my own. Good friends appreciate you for your sense of humor, your ability to keep secrets, your goofiness—not typically for your looks. Loving peer and adult presence are invaluable resources for kids and teens. They are antidotes to the voices who say that your worth is in your beauty or your ability to have six-pack abs or your body being thin. Nothing counteracts one-dimensional screen images than real, live people who love you for who you are inside and out. Any time your kids or teens can be around people like this is gold. Community is powerful and healing. I see it in my group work with clients, and I know this implicitly from my own life's work.

Step 7: References and Resources

Common Sense Media, 2015 Report. https://www.comm
onsensemedia.org/

Damiano, S., Paxton S.J., Wertheim, E.H., McLean, S.A.,
and Gregg, K.J. "Dietary restraint of 5-year-old girls:
Associations with internalization of the thin ideal and
maternal, media, and peer influences." *International Journal
of Eating Disorders.* 2015;48(8):1166–1169.

Spiel E.C., Paxton S.J., and Yager, Z. "Weight attitudes in 3- to
5-year-old children: Age differences and cross-sectional
predictors." *Body Image.* 2012;9(4):524–527.

Tzoutzou, M., Bathrelllou, E., and Matalas, A. "Body weight
of cartoon characters in children's series is associated to
food consumption, attractiveness, and physical-activity
engagement." *International Journal of Behavioral Medicine.*
2020;27:707–716.

McLean, S., Jarmen, H., and Rodgers, R. "How do 'selfies' impact
adolescents' well-being and body confidence? A narrative
review." *Psychology Research and Behavior Management.*
2019;12:513–521.

Taylor, S.R. *The Body Is Not an Apology: The Power of Radical
Self-Love.* Oakland, CA: Berrett-Koehler Publishers, Inc.;
2018.

The Alliance for Eating Disorders https://www.alliancefo
reatingdisorders.com/resource-library/

The Multi-Service Eating Disorders Association (MEDA) https://www.medainc.org/

Body Positive/Neutral Instagram Accounts (as of the publishing of this book):

- @amypoehlersmartgirls

- @mynameisjessamyn

- @iheartericka

- @notplantbased

- @theshirarose

- @theselfloveproject

Body Positive/Neutral Podcasts (as of the publishing of this book):

- Food Psych/Rethinking Wellness

- Burnt Toast

- Eat the Rules

- Nutrition Matters

- Break the Diet Cycle

- Living in a Queer Body

- The Body Image Podcast

- Body Positivity Podcast

Step 7

- The Full Bloom Podcast

Yoga Resources for People in All-Size Bodies on YouTube (as of the publishing of this book):

- Jessamyn Stanley, Underbelly Yoga

- Tiffany Croww

- Yoga with Zelinda

- Reyna Cohan

STEP 8
Cultivate Sustaining Self-Care Practices

"Mom, you are so annoying.
I am totally freaking out, and you're all chill and calm.
It drives me effing crazy."

~ Kyla, age 16 (who secretly appreciated her mom's chillness)

I have learned that our main job as parents of teens is to completely embarrass and annoy the heck out of them. If we do our job well, then they will be able to separate effectively.

Well, that's a gross oversimplification of the developmental stage of an adolescent, one where the teen spreads their wings and separates from family of origin to form a more coherent sense of self. He/she/they will adopt some of the ways of the family and reject some of the ways of the family, eventually landing on a sense of self that is all their own. As parents, we have to sit back and enjoy the wild ride while our teens try on different identities, fashion, and friends. There's not a lot that we can or should do about this very individual process.

One thing that we can do as parents, which many of us who discuss these things have determined (namely, my therapist friends who happen to be parents), is to get very grounded ourselves in who we are, what our values are, and be consistent in our own identity. Not that we can't pivot and change our minds, but modeling a coherent sense of self is good for our kids. That said, setting limits on teens' boundless boundary-testing is very important, too. We can do this well only if we know first what our own limits are.

Even though children and teens may not like our limits and demeanor, being ourselves as parents and not compromising who we are (even when our instant-gratification-oriented young ones want us to) is critical for encouraging our kids to be who they truly are inside. If we don't do this as parents and caretakers, our kids will easily find other role models who they admire to emulate and take after. They may do this even when we provide solid role-modeling, but perhaps it's less critical. Teens explore lots of different sides of themselves, coming back to some of the foundational values of their families—if those values were taught in a way that allowed for free will and if the family expression of those values was not harmful or traumatic in the young person's eyes.

This chapter's step toward raising kids who are balanced around food, body, and self is about *care of the self*. We will best encourage kids of all ages to care well for themselves (around food and the rest of life) if we do so ourselves and they are left to imitate us at will. And, yes, this imitation will come and go. My teens used to make fun of my "hippie clothes," and now they shop at thrift stores, too, because they understand the value and fun of finding one-of-a-kind vintage items. As a tween, one of my daughters once asked me if I would please start dressing like "other moms." My response: "Would you like me to dress like other moms, or would you like me to dress like myself?" The sheepish response: "Yourself." I rest my case.

By being strong in my own sense of self, not wavering because someone I love wants me to present in a different way, I aim to give my daughters an example of someone who knows herself and her own style. My hope is that it helps free them up to cultivate their own sense of self and style—particularly important in my family because my daughters are twins.

I wasn't always so strong in my own sense of self, by the way. I have had the privilege of time and resources to do the therapy and personal-growth work that have brought me to this generally centered and strong place. And, yes, I still have my moments of wavering self-doubt. **Doing my own internal work has been as good for my family as it has been for me**.

During the late-teen years, when I experienced my daughters wondering about and experimenting more with alcohol and sexual activity, we kept the dialogue about those topics wide open. Yes, I sometimes made them cringe, but no topic was taboo. I believe this has kept communication open between all of us. If I talked about my own lessons learned around substance use and sex, then they felt open to talk about theirs. This doesn't mean that I shared every detail and made the conversation all about me. However, a little lived experience in the mix goes a long way toward eliminating the shame that lots of teens have around lots of subjects. I've always reminded them (and their friends) that our house is a "judgment-free zone." That said, I'm still the parent, and I'm going to set limits and address issues of self-care and impulsive behavior so that lessons can be learned.

While the teen years of parenting are "fresh" in my awareness right now, I recall that throughout my children's growing, it was important for me to check in with myself often and make sure that I was taking good care of myself. (After all, no one else will do it better.) Sometimes I was doing a great job of this, and, sometimes, it was abysmal. Yes, even someone who encourages self-care practices in others might have struggles around this herself. Many of us in the helping professions got here honestly, working through some of the exact issues that we now help others to navigate.

I believe that every time I returned to taking care of myself, setting boundaries, and trying to embody warrior mama, my daughters watched this carefully. They learned a bit about the value of including oneself in the care and energy we give out to the world. I believe this is particularly important for those who identify as female, as women are still encouraged by society to carry a load of family and work responsibilities with grace and glamour. When I decided to make my work schedule lighter so that I had more time for family and peace of mind, my daughters paid attention. Yes, I had the privilege of working for myself and being able to do so. Given that we live in a high-achieving, work-driven northeastern U.S. suburb, witnessing me striving to find balance in this intellect-celebrating, hustle-and-grind culture is something I hope they took in. I see glimpses of it here and there when I hear them talk about wanting "downtime" and creating that for themselves in their busy activity-filled weeks.

Enough about my own experience, though it's certainly what I'm most familiar with, and so I share it. I've created this step about cultivating sustainable self-care practices for individuals in my first book, *Nourish,* and now for families in *Nurture,* because I believe that it's a buffer against disordered eating, as well as body preoccupation and loathing. Why? First, I use the term "practices" instead of "habits" or "routines," because the word indicates that you are trying something new and may need to keep at it for a while for that something new to become a habit. A wise mentor and African Healing Dance teacher, Wyoma, introduced me to the concept of establishing daily practices that sustain mind, body, and spirit. First you must get in touch with your values and what nourishes you deeply. (See Step 7 in *Nourish* if you want to investigate this further.) Then, you are ready to create activities in your life and family that reflect those values.

Teaching kids about values, and building practices as a family that connect to those values, is very grounding for young people. Even if they eventually turn away from some of those practices and create some different ones of their own, particularly in adolescence, teaching kids to appreciate self-care and values-based choices will help them create a life that is joyful and fully their own. Yes, we all have to work and make a living, but we can more consciously choose that path to living and working when we value care of the self in these choices.

I don't like the way the diet and beauty industries have co-opted the term "self-care" to get us to buy their products. When I talk about self-care, I mean aligning with who you are as an individual, choosing to live your life from that place, and creating regular practices in life that remind you of what's important. And, ideally, we don't stop with the "self" in self-care. When we are aligned with ourselves and our purpose on this planet, then we naturally extend ourselves outward toward others in ways that reflect who we are and what we have to offer.

Yes, self-care is not selfish, and it's not limited to just caring for number one. **By putting our own needs and purpose in the daily mix—something that is hard for many parents to do—we often find that we have more to offer those we love and care for.** I've worked with parents who have found a craft, sport, drum, dance class, or meditation practice, added daily or weekly, to be a balm that balances the sometimes mundane and repetitive nature of the tasks inherent in parenting. Finding an individual passion, no matter how "good" at it they are, connects them to the individual inside the caretaker. When we do things we love and enjoy regularly, we feel more fulfilled—and we are less likely to use food (binging or restriction) to feel better.

I want to acknowledge again that many of my clients have a great deal of privilege in being able to make these kinds of values-based choices in life, as do many of you. Those of us who are white, cis-gendered, heterosexual, able-bodied, financially stable, thin, and learn in the typical ways of academic learning have an easier time with most of the systems in place in our society. We have an advantage in being able to create the time, space, and energy to engage in self-care practices and choices. We must not forget this, particularly when we find ourselves judging another human being who has less privilege.

Many of the adolescents I have seen in my nutrition-therapy practice who struggle with eating disorders are burned out. They are in their junior or senior years of high school, stressing about grades, whether they have enough extra-curricular activities to make it into college, and many social pressures. They are often juggling jobs, community service, and hours of homework as well as full school days. When I heard from an Adolescent Medicine doctor that teens need nine to ten hours of sleep, I laughed heartily, as teens in my community are typically under-slept and overworked. They haven't learned good self-care practices because there is almost no time to have them—and often the high-powered parents around them are modeling the same. I witness workaholism being passed down from generation to generation. While hard work should be applauded and innovation requires time and grit, hard work without balance leads to burnout for most.

My practice office has been located near Ivy league and other very competitive colleges around Boston, Massachusetts. When I see college students, I hear them say that university life is "easier than high school," mainly because there is more time in the day to complete work and have a balanced life. It's sad that high-school kids are pushed to cram so much into a day when their brains and bodies are working overtime to just *grow*. Adolescence is the second most rapid time of growth for humans (the first being infancy). Why are we overloading teens when they need the extra rest and energy for growth and brain development?

I believe that many of our chronic diseases, mental illnesses, and growing fatigues can be boiled down to deficits in self-care. If we are part of an oppressed or under-represented group in society because of race, gender, sexual orientation, body size, physical ability, mental ability, or learning style, then it can be even more difficult to get care for the self or from others that we equally deserve. Deficits in self-care include failing to check in with ourselves during the day around what we need, appreciating what we are feeling, and knowing when enough is enough.

Sometimes we or our children get to the end of the day and feel depleted. We eat as a reward or treat—or to give ourselves something good when the day has left us little energy for anything else. Or, conversely, we restrict or obsess about our food intake or bodies as a way to feel better about or feel more in control of our lives. Teens in my clinical practice often don't realize they are doing this until they examine it closely.

Whether we want it to be or not, food will always be associated with love and care, as well as a response to appetite. It has been so since the time that we cried for our birth mother's care and feeding on our first day as a human being. Catherine Cook-Cottone, who has looked extensively at self-care and prevention of eating disorders, believes that eating disorders are, in their most basic form, a collection of embodied, physical acts that function to help an individual manage what feels like overwhelming internal and external stresses and demands.

Step 8

Teens and adults with eating disorders are doing two seemingly opposing things. Psychologically, they are leaving themselves by avoiding the authentic experience of their bodies, feelings, and thoughts. At the same time, their eating disorders actively engage them in a pathological relationship with their bodies that is both cognitively and emotionally intense. My clients with disordered eating are constantly thinking about and distracted by body sensations (like weight, shape, size, bloating, consequences of restriction or frantic eating, etc.) and constantly having feelings and judgments about their bodies. This is the view of the "embodied self" that she/he/they can control.

Eating disorder recovery and prevention efforts, therefore, need to address this *relationship with the body*, as this is where the disorder begins. To recover, or avoid illness in the first place, one must learn to be with and in their bodies in a healthy and effective way. Research shows us that resilient children and adolescents know how to effectively and positively manage internal feelings and external pressures as fully embodied experiences. When development and experience are "normal," children do not necessarily notice or think about their bodies as they are busy eating and functioning in the world. Researcher Cook-Cottone believes that we can teach children positive self-care practices and ways of being that move them toward a life of embodied self-regulation and body appreciation.

Trouble with **self-regulation** is central to eating-disorders risk and to the emergence of symptoms across all three of the major types of eating disorders: anorexia nervosa, bulimia nervosa, and binge-eating disorder. To prevent and treat eating disorders, individuals must learn how to negotiate life without leaving themselves or turning against the body. As Cook-Cottone says, "The way out is in."

Neuroscience supports this, too, as self-regulation, particularly emotion regulation, involves integrated activity throughout the whole brain. Self-regulation occurs in both directions: how we think affects how we experience our feelings and bodies, and how we experience our feelings and bodies affects how we think. We can change how we experience the world by shifting our thoughts and also by shifting our embodied actions. Researcher Stice and colleagues noted that eating-disorders prevention efforts that just target the thin ideal do not seem to have robust and long-term effects, indicating that preventing eating disorders must address more than just thinking/cognition.

Cook-Cottone further reports on research that shows children can be taught self-regulation and self-care (for example, active yoga practice, relaxation strategies, meditation, feeling identification, and coping) and that this is likely helpful in preventing internalization of the thin ideal, development of poor body image, and self-objectification. These negatives particularly happen during late adolescence into adulthood, when eating-disordered behaviors often develop. Improvements in self-regulation can be preventative as early as first grade, according to the research. Cook-Cottone argues that, along with cognitive thinking-focused work around media literacy, which is effective for older populations, we should add efforts to improve embodied self-regulation and self-care for younger children.

What does this look like? We can teach our young people (and, perhaps, first ourselves) to pause daily to check in and ask what we are feeling. We can learn to use compassion to reflect on our challenges and difficulties with kindness. We can make sure that we eat, hydrate, and rest regularly. We can make a point of cultivating supportive relationships and setting personal boundaries. We can learn active mind-body practices like yoga and meditation in its many forms (finding one that suits us) to enhance self-regulation. Kids watch and imitate the adults around them. **If you practice good self-care, showing authentic appreciation of your body and mind and energy by being in your body in a mindful, present, and caring way, then your children will be watching and learning. As always, we don't have to be perfect. Striving is typically enough.**

We can't ignore the research that shows eating disorders have a genetic component. Some kids are more wired at birth to develop challenges around anxiety, depression, and body image, despite our best intentions as parents and caregivers. However, if parents, schools, and other systems around children encourage embodied self-care, we might protect those children who are more vulnerable.

When it comes to food, teaching children to make food choices from a place of self-care and listening to the body can't be stressed enough. As I highlighted in previous steps, don't impose your eating style on your kids, as they may have very different preferences and bodies. Encourage them to celebrate their own unique preferences and eat things they like. Share your own preferences for food, movement, and self-care with your children, but let them discover their own preferences, too.

Give your kids plenty of opportunities to explore different ways to work, play, and care for their unique selves. Give them space to get bored and explore (ideally away from a cell phone) so they can learn about what lights them up, gives them energy, and allows them to rest and restore. I can't say enough about how important this is in our fast-paced, work-oriented culture. We can't protect our children from their genetic inheritance or the hardships of life, but we can give them skills to resource themselves so that they have the capacity to meet challenges.

Step 8: References and Resources

Schauster, H. *Nourish: How to Heal Your Relationship with Food, Body, and Self.* Somerville, MA: Hummingbird Press, 2018.

Cook-Cottone, C.P. "Embodied self-regulation and mindful self-care in the prevention of eating disorders." *Journal of Eating Disorders.* 2016;24(1):98–105.

Cook-Cottone, C.P. "Incorporating positive body image into the treatment of eating disorders: A model for attunement and mindful self-care." *Body Image.* 2015;14:158–167.

Piran, N. and Teall, T. "The developmental theory of embodiment." In. G. McVey, P. Levine, N. Piran, and H.P. Ferguson (Eds.) *Preventing Eating-related and Weight-related Disorders:*

Collaborative Research, Advocacy, and Policy Change. Waterloo, ON: Wilfred Laurier Press. 2012;171–199.

Alleva J.M., Sheeran, P., Webb, T.L., Martijn, C., and Miles, E. "A meta-analytic review of stand-alone interventions to improve body image." *PLOS One.* 10(9); e)139177.

Stice, E., Rohde, P., Butryn, M.L., Shaw, H., and Marti, C.N. "Effectiveness trial of a selective dissonance-based eating disorder prevention program with female college students: effects at 2- and 3-year follow-up." *Behaviour Research and Therapy.* 2015;71:20–26.

Cook-Cottone, C.P., Tribole, E., and Tylka, T.L. *Healthy eating in schools: Evidence-based interventions to help kids thrive.* American Psychological Association. 2013. https://doi.org/10.1037/14180–000

Siegel, D. *Brainstorm: The Power and Purpose of the Teenage Brain.* New York, NY: Penguin Random House, 2015.

STEP 9

Teach Young People That Feelings Are Safe

"My head is getting all muddled, and I forgot my think, and my mouth just keeps on talking."

~ Ava, age 5

Why do we need to talk about feelings in a book about feeding our families and cultivating healthy body image? If it's not already clear, hopefully, this Step will make it clear that eating and emotions can be tangled. The quote above shows that articulating feelings can be challenging for little ones. Ava's creative description of anxiety, as it showed up in her little body, was astonishingly accurate.

Emotions arise for important reasons. Over our lifetimes, we ideally learn to identify our feelings, learn from them, and use them to help us do meaningful things. Our children—and maybe even our adult selves—are bumbling around in the world doing this. Emotions can be helpful and informative, but they can also be scary or threatening, particularly if they aren't given proper space, or we've learned that they are dangerous from adults, caregivers, and communities before us.

Dr. Jill Bolte Taylor, a Harvard brain scientist, has been credited with discovering that emotions last roughly ninety seconds in the body. Incredible. Ninety seconds is all it takes to identify an emotion and allow it to dissipate while you notice it. When you're stressed, pausing for ninety seconds and labeling what you are feeling (for example, *"I'm feeling angry"*) decreases the activity in the amygdala of the brain, the part responsible for our fight-or-flight fear and stress response. **It's not our emotions that are problematic for us. Our thinking and ruminating about what we are feeling typically get us into trouble and make us feel stuck.**

Moods and emotional states lasting longer than ninety seconds may occur due to life events, social factors like work or school conditions, watching the news, trauma history, illness, life transitions like growth spurts or hormonal shifts, and more. Helping your children and teens to notice their feelings and tolerate them does them a service. So many of us learned that feelings or emotions (particularly the "negative" ones like anger, sadness, or frustration, for example) are intolerable or to be avoided because they are "too much" for one to handle. Yes, some bodies and minds have more intense emotional experiences than others. Still, most importantly, children—and adults—need to know that their emotions make sense and that these feelings communicate something important.

I highly recommend the "Feelings Inventory," published by the Center for Nonviolent Communication at https://www.cnvc.org/store/feelings-and-needs-inventory. It's an extensive list of words we can use to express a combination of emotional states and physical sensations. Though not exhaustive or definitive, it's an excellent place to start when we are trying to communicate feeling states to another person or to teach kids about feelings. There are two parts to the list: feelings we may have when our needs are being met (for example: blissful, engaged, or peaceful) and feelings we may have when our needs are not being met (for example: scared, disconnected, sad, or angry). Naming and communicating feelings helps us to not become overwhelmed by sensations that arise, often without warning or apparent reason.

Feelings or emotions are generally attached to body sensations. They also communicate needs and desires underneath the sensations. Anxiety and fear are best not ignored. They are symptoms and expressions of something important. Emotions can trigger the nervous system to respond in a particular way for a specific reason. There is learning there. Tolerating the emotion and spending time with it to understand it can be helpful.

When your child feels a fluttery nervousness before a family gathering, he may be expressing some shyness or need for self-expression, which is hard among family members. When another child feels angry after a playdate, she may feel hurt, tired, or need de-stimulation and quiet. She may not be able to articulate that, but a pointed question from a caregiver who suspects the need or feeling that might be present can help. "I wonder if you would like to lie down and rest after your playdate." It's up to the child to respond and follow through, but noticing your child's feeling state can be validating.

Knowing that emotion can be addressed more fully and personally under the right conditions is a skill in patience and psychological flexibility. **We do well by the young people in our lives when we aren't afraid to talk about emotions, especially when the heat of the moment has passed.** Sometimes adults need to take time out to allow self-regulation before lashing out at another family member. Taking that pause but returning to talk about why we felt angry or disappointed— giving feelings the light of day in a way that does no harm but acknowledges feelings that are present and valid—is a great way to teach children that emotions can be tolerated and are essential to communicate and address. If adults do have an impulsive, dysregulated reaction, it is a powerful teaching moment to own the mistake, apologize to children, and explain what was trying to be expressed. ("I was worried about a work project. I was impatient, lashed out at your mother, and I am very sorry. It was not the best way to express what I was feeling.")

My two daughters are different when it comes to emotions. They both feel things, but how they respond to their emotions has differed since the beginning of their lives. As I've mentioned, they are fraternal twins (not identical), like night and day about many things. While one sister was having toddler tantrums, the other looked at her sister like, "What's the big deal?" because she moved on from upsets more easily and seemed not to feel them in such a whole-bodied way. Their nervous systems were very different from infancy. The sister who tended to tantrum was a colic-y baby who later woke many nights from nightmares, while her more even-tempered twin could fall asleep anywhere and slept through the night easily. I had the benefit of raising two identically aged children and seeing how different they could be—even in the same environment. (It helped me not take credit for too much.) Now that I'm studying Somatic Experiencing (SE), I understand them as having different nervous systems, which were distinct since their birth.

Whether your children are more chill and easygoing or fiery and expressive, they deserve to appreciate the emotions that arise inside them. It's a skill to tolerate and not get overwhelmed by an emotional state. The best way to communicate to your children that their emotions are not too much is not to make too much of them yourself. When children are getting anxious or activated, as parents, we do best by grounding ourselves, staying calm, and teaching them that their emotions are okay. "I feel angry about what happened, too. It might take a little while for our bodies to settle and feel ready to move on. Let's see if we can find something else to do this afternoon." If the child escalates the tantrum: "I see how upset you are. I'm going to do some laundry/wash dishes/listen to a book or music and will be right here. When both of our bodies are feeling ready to move on, we'll figure out what to play with next." The feeling is labeled, and time is calmly given to allow the emotion to process through.

In these statements, we teach a young child that emotions are commonplace, that the caregiver can handle their own and the child's emotions, and that difficult feelings subside eventually. It can be tough to do this when we, as caregivers, feel activated ourselves. I'll own that it's easy for me to write about this. Putting it into practice as a parent is quite another story. Even the most unruffled parents lose it sometimes. When that happens, it helps to name the feeling and apologize. "Mommy was so angry and scared. I wish that I had talked to you more gently. I'm sorry."

This statement teaches kids that even grown-ups have trouble when emotions are high, but that repair can be done. If this happens occasionally, it allows rupture/repair work that is healing and builds strength in the relationship. Constant yelling at a child, on the other hand, can be confusing and traumatic to a young nervous system. We have to be compassionate with ourselves about these very human parenting moments. We might need time out, a break, or some support. Sometimes the parent is best served by getting some professional help to prevent this behavior from occurring regularly. It will do the parent and child well to find other ways to tolerate and discharge emotion and tension. We grow through our successes and our mistakes. Teaching children to process mistakes in an affirming, self-respecting way is an important life skill to pass on.

Some families are more expressive of feelings, and some less so. There is no right or wrong way to have emotions, but there are more respectful ways to work through and express them, particularly the more intense ones. Some families unintentionally create patterns where food is used for comfort when emotions run high. This may happen when food is used as a reward for good behavior, or there is a culture of stuffing down feelings.

Do you remember Amelia and her daughter Sophie from Step 3? Amelia was worried for her daughter because she seemed obsessed with bread and cheese as a nine-year-old—after eating a gluten-free and dairy-free diet for most of her childhood. One thing Amelia did well was encouraging Sophie to have a full range of feelings. This is not easy as a parent. It breaks our hearts to see our kids' hearts break. Amelia noticed that Sophie tended to "stuff" down feelings, possibly using food for comfort and avoiding discussion of sad or difficult material. Amelia has reminded Sophie that feeling sad, angry, jealous, frustrated, or confused is okay—and part of being human.

Remember how Sophie nearly panicked on her way to dance class if her mom didn't have a snack for her? She asked, "Did you bring me a snack? Is this all? I told you I'm *really* hungry!" Some of this food angst might have been related to the charge around food and the deprivation mindset from years of watching the other kids eat sandwiches while Sophie had to eat a special diet. I've observed that many kids with multiple food allergies feel insecure and anxious about food. This makes sense because eating the wrong thing could cause an itchy rash, a swollen tongue, or a life-threatening reaction. Sophie was encouraged to follow a similarly limited diet. At times, Sophie may not have had enough to eat, making her feel stressed and ravenous. Amelia also witnessed that Sophie struggles during transitions, using food to ground her. When well-fed, she feels cared for and less distracted by the discomfort of hunger.

All humans want to feel taken care of. We want to feel like we have enough. Kids sometimes crave and hoard food because it's soothing and grounding during overthinking or anxiety. Food brings us into our bodies and senses (and out of our minds), so it can be a reprieve from an overactive noggin to eat something delicious. When I work with adults to include other "sensory delights" in their day (for example, taking a pause from work to step outside and take in the fresh air and the beauty of trees, burning a scented candle, or wrapping themselves in soft fabric), their over-reliance on food for sensory input and downtime often shifts. Clients frequently don't realize that they use food to give their brains a break. They've never considered other ways to take a break when it's needed.

Munching on food or restricting food can be a soothing habit and a way to discharge activation and anxiety in the body. While there's nothing wrong with using food to soothe and ground, there are lots of ways to resource the body and mind. Eating beyond comfortable fullness or starving your tissues repeatedly means that you might be using the pleasurable sensations of eating or (for some) starving in a way that does not ultimately care for the body. You may miss out on other ways to express anxiety or care for your mind and body. Emotions are instructive. Often, they point us to needs that aren't being met. When we feel anxious, we may be feeling a need for self-expression or safety. When we feel bored, we may be expressing a need for more stimulation or connection. **If you "numb" out with food or food restriction (or anything else), then you may be missing out on expressing emotions,**

**meeting the needs underneath, and seeking out other ways
to meet those needs besides using food.**

Again, so-called "emotional eating" is not the problem.
(If you eat birthday cake to celebrate, you emotionally eat.
We all do at times.) The issue is the possibility of feelings
that might not be expressed and more completely dealt with
if food is always the go-to. Eating beyond fullness can be part
of normal eating. I do it when the food tastes delicious, or I'm
distracted by other things and don't notice fullness cues. But
I don't do it repeatedly and ritually like when I struggled with
binge eating in my late teens and early college years, due to
intermittently underfeeding my body and struggling to express
painful and confusing feelings.

I prefer that clients working with me on their relationships with food in my nutrition-therapy practice also have
psychotherapists who can help them diagnose, manage, and
improve mental-health issues, often at the root of problems
around imbalance with food. Imbalance includes both under-
eating, over-eating, and switching back and forth between
the two. If you notice that your child or teen has a complicated relationship with food or exercise, it can be helpful to
start with a psychotherapist who can help determine if there
is some underlying depression, anxiety, trauma responses,
obsessive-compulsive tendencies, or other mood disorders. In
addition, it can be beneficial to consult with a neuropsycholo-
gist to determine if ADD/ADHD, processing issues, or other
neurodivergence may be contributing to dysregulated eating.
Giving children and teens a place to acknowledge and talk
about their feelings—whether with a parent, another trusted

adult (often more beneficial for teens than their parents), or a psychotherapist—is like permitting them to be human.

We all sometimes need help with difficult situations, and we are all together on this planet. We are not meant to be islands, keeping our feelings locked inside. Learning to feel, express, and move on from difficult emotions is a skill. It's taught to children by example from adults who don't react—but allow—true emotional expression. This can be hard to do if you are a parent tangled up by your kids' emotions, which is why a therapist or other adult can sometimes be a godsend. It genuinely "takes a village" to raise children, and there should be no shame in asking for help from other adults or trusted professionals. I always say that asking for help is a heroic act.

Remember that food has represented care and comfort since our first days after birth. Food and love are entwined, whether we want them to be or not, so when we have some challenges with feeling loved or cared for, food often enters as a soother. **When our nervous systems are trying to negotiate and integrate a traumatic event or series of events, food (compulsive eating or over-control and restriction) can be a way to numb out or feel safety and pleasure.** It's not a problem to eat for comfort on occasion, but if food is standing in for emotional expression or more effective ways to cope with challenges in life, then your child or teen may be missing out. I can't say enough that it's important not to make food and "willpower" around food the problem. The problem is around coping with difficult emotions and circumstances.

So many of us adults use food to feel soothed or in control of our emotions. I recommend that we help kids learn to recognize and tolerate emotion—to self-regulate and come back to balance—so that food doesn't need to get mixed up here. We need to help our children learn what to do with angry feelings, sad feelings, and feelings of disappointment so that they don't need to use food (or a more dangerous substance) as a way to escape or manage. Sometimes, as caregivers, we must learn to do this ourselves first. Self-regulation includes building resources and resilience for dealing with difficult emotions and environments.

The resources that build resilience are very individual. When I'm angry, hurt, or scared, for example, I resource by connecting with nature, writing about my feelings, or processing them aloud (or in writing) with someone I trust. I also ground myself by using my body (feeling my feet on the floor and noticing the support of the chair underneath me). When I need some significant grounding and resourcing and have the space, I dance. When my partner was in the hospital on a ventilator for two weeks after a surgical complication, I managed this rough time by getting up at sunrise and "dancing my prayers." These resourcing techniques might not work for everyone—or anyone else, for that matter—but finding the resources that do work for you is essential for helping you ride the waves of emotion when events are significant or challenging. Helping your children develop resiliency in the face of difficulty includes pointing out the times when they are effectively coping and urging them to use those strategies when they feel off-balance.

During the pandemic year of 2020, when children and teens were staying home and doing school online instead of being in the natural social milieu with peers, my 16-year-old daughter Kyla said she felt angry and frustrated every day. Kyla told me she "stuffed it down" because she thought she might hurt someone otherwise. My typically gentle daughter was feeling the stress of adolescence compounded by a pandemic. We talked openly about it being okay to be angry and about channeling that anger to action and sometimes social action. It is also okay to express the anger, get it out, and do nothing with it except having self-awareness, an admirable trait in itself. When angry feelings get stuck in our bodies, and we don't have an outlet, it can be destructive to others and ourselves.

My daughter and I discussed the possibility of seeing a psychotherapist and, brilliantly, Kyla suggested that maybe a punching bag would help her not slug her twin sister. We decided to put a punching bag in the basement and connected Kyla with a boxing coach who was doing private lessons during the pandemic because he couldn't hold live group classes. It was the best intervention for my active daughter, who needed some full-bodied release of tension. She finds using her body easier than using words to express feelings. (She once was the toddler who occasionally had tantrums with her whole body when upset.) Being cooped up in her bedroom doing online school was taking its toll. Kyla and I decided that if the physical outlet of boxing and talking about her feelings with her mom (or her friends or one of my adult friends) was not helping her feel more regulated, we'd reach out to a psychotherapist.

When emotions are acceptable and tolerable, children and teens learn how to bring themselves back to balance from dysregulating emotions and learn valuable life skills. They are also less likely to eat frantically when stressed or use dieting and food restriction to feel better or more in control. I work with clients of all ages who struggle with their relationships with food. It's incredible how much problematic food behaviors lessen when they learn to tolerate feelings of activation and anxiety, resource themselves, and return to calm and emotional self-regulation.

I want to note here that "fat" is not a feeling. I encourage teens and adults who "feel fat" to get curious and ask themselves what emotions may be coming up in their bodies. Sadly, "fat" has become a negative word in our culture. Instead of being a neutral body type descriptor, "fat" is often used to express a negative judgment about the body in this thinness- and diet-obsessed culture. We already talked about the oppressiveness of equating "fat" with negativity in Step 2. I often hear "I feel gross" or "I feel bloated" from clients. Often, we embody our feelings and focus on the body and its supposed flaws.

What emotions might arise if you weren't focused on your body's appearance? Fear? Anger? Disgust? Shame? I then ask clients to locate that emotion in the body. Anxiety is often felt in the chest or the head; sadness sometimes resides in the pit of the stomach. Everyone feels emotions a little differently, and I find this fascinating. I get more curious if the feeling can be located in the body. Does it have a shape, color, texture, movement, or other quality? If they can answer these questions, clients demonstrate that, if only for moments, they can tolerate difficult emotions. They might allow the feeling to rise and fall like a wave, letting it move through them until they return to neutral.

I want to mention a bit about trauma and the body. Many books will have more to say about this topic, and I list some excellent resources at the end of this chapter. Sometimes body discomfort and negative feelings about the body are related to trauma, such as physical or sexual abuse. Some of us experience the significant trauma of oppression due to the social constructs of race, gender, ability, health, body size, and cultural ideals of beauty. When our bodies have been betrayed, we can disconnect from them and distrust them even more. Sometimes when our boundaries have been violated, we try to make ourselves unattractive—consciously or unconsciously—so that it won't happen again.

Healing from trauma and integrating the experience to learn to love and care for our bodies and selves is an integral part of the process for some. If your or your child's body has been traumatized, healing work that ultimately moves you or your loved one toward gentleness with self will help significantly toward a healthier connection with the body.

It's also important to note that not all children and adults find access to feelings and emotions easy, particularly those on the autism spectrum. While a discussion of these challenges is beyond the scope of this book, and there are many more qualified individuals who can address the concerns of this population, I encourage parents and caregivers to appreciate these differences and the unique circumstances that we and our children inherit.

Healthy body connection ultimately requires letting go of the idea that our bodies are wrong and need fixing.

Then, and only then, can we make choices from a place of self-love, self-respect, and self-care instead of a place of "something's wrong." Compassion is a more potent motivator than self-criticism. Why? According to Kristin Neff, author of the book *Self-Compassion*, "Because its driving force is love, not fear." Loving ourselves (body, mind, and spirit) and loving the children in our care is vital.

Don't fret if you don't always say the perfect thing to your child. Talking about feelings can be tricky, especially if you are out of practice. Stumbling and showing your kids you are vulnerable and doing your best is okay. If you love your children, and they see you striving to do your best as a parent, I believe that is worth volumes.

Step 9: References and Resources

The Center for Nonviolent Communication "Feelings Inventory": https://www.cnvc.org/store/feelings-and-needs-inventory

National Child Traumatic Stress Network (NCTSN) https://www.nctsn.org/

Selvam, R. *The Practice of Embodying Emotions: A Guide for Improving Cognitive, Emotional, and Behavioral Outcomes.* Berkeley, CA: North Atlantic Books, 2022.

Levine, P. *Waking the Tiger: Healing Trauma.* Berkeley, CA: North Atlantic Books, 1997.

Levine, P. *In an Unspoken Voice: How the Body Releases Trauma and Restores Goodness.* Berkeley, CA: North Atlantic Books, 2010.

Levine, P. and Kline, M. *Trauma Through a Child's Eyes: Awakening the Ordinary Miracle of Healing.* Berkeley, CA: North Atlantic Books, 2019.

van der Kolk, B. *The Body Keeps the Score: Brain, Mind, and Body in the Healing of Trauma.* New York, NY: Penguin Books, 2014.

Neff, K. *Self-Compassion: The Proven Power of Being Kind to Yourself.* New York, NY: Harper Collins Publishers, 2011.

STEP 10

Spotlight Whole Self and Embodiment

"... The undulating of my mother's belly was not
a shame she hid from her children.
She knew we came from this. Her belly was a gift
we kept passing between us. ..."

~ Sonya Renee Taylor, excerpt from the poem "My Mother's Belly"

I love these lines from a poem that opens Sonya Renee Taylor's excellent book, *The Body is Not an Apology*. We come to the final Step in what I hope has been a compassionate guide for parents and caregivers. As mentioned, these steps are not linear or ordered by importance. I think this last step is the most critical, as the other nine steps branch out from its strong root ball. Step 10 assists you in encouraging young people to accept the importance of the whole self over body and appearances, despite the culture around them that often pushes for the opposite. We may have to constantly remind our children that their body is just one facet of the self. Their spirit, their soul, their essence (or whatever term you like) is within them, and that is their truest nature.

When I start each session of my therapeutic book clubs, I do a somatically oriented meditation practice to help the group members get grounded and connect to themselves before they connect with others. I like to introduce into my meditations the concept that our physical body is contained within our subtle body or self, including our personality, sense of humor, unique qualities, and quirks. I ask them to imagine the space around their physical bodies, which contains all these other diverse elements of the self. I ask them to imagine that they are thoroughly filling that space, inhabiting it all. "Taking up space," physically, emotionally, and spiritually, is not always encouraged in a culture that still values small, docile bodies, particularly among those who identify as women.

Your body and the way that you choose to adorn your body may reflect your values and spirit, but your body is not all of who you are. When my clients become more whole-self-focused and less body-focused, they allow themselves to take up space. They speak up more, set boundaries on their time and energy, and make decisions aligned with their own needs and preferences and those of others. They eat in a way that aligns with their self-care and move in ways that feel right and feed their souls. They no longer eat or exercise in "I should" ways but in "I want" ways. The distinction is significant, as the behaviors are connected to the self's particular needs and appetites as opposed to pleasing or copying others.

162

It would be very natural for parents and caregivers, in focusing on healthy body image for your children, that your own issues around body image may come up. As the saying goes, we need to put on our own oxygen mask before we can effectively take care of those we love. You deserve to have the same ease and gentle relationship with your body that you want your children to have. It may be healing to have a few sessions yourself with a therapist who works with body image and disordered eating. Much of therapy is virtual today, so it could have a profound impact without having to be very long-term or cumbersome.

Before we talk about the "whole self" of your child, I want to say a few words about how important it is to teach kids how appearances change while they grow. Growth spurts can happen anytime, though they more predictably increase in the teen years. Growing is more than just getting taller. Growth can mean getting fuller and rounder, and this should be normalized so that it's not "bad" or "wrong." Friends all grow at different times and rates. Even siblings, like my own fraternal twin daughters, grow uniquely. Puberty will not necessarily happen to friends or siblings simultaneously, and this can be a source of shame or confusion for a child who doesn't seem to be progressing like their peers.

In the back seat of my car, I listened to many little girls talk about their round tummies. I frequently turned my head to remind these pre-pubertal girls that their round bellies were necessary for growth and would help them eventually develop into the bodies of young women. When I meet with menopausal women at the decline of their estrogen years, they also lament about some roundness around their middle. Again, this is perfectly normal and protective at this time of life. We know that extreme thinness is dangerous in older adults and that those who fall into the "overweight" BMI category have the best life expectancy from all causes of mortality. Some roundness in the middle protects delicate organs. So, why do we call this category "overweight" if it has the best health outcomes? (I wrote about this dilemma at length in Step 2.)

Understanding that some kids are naturally rounder and fatter than others helps to normalize and not demonize fat. Understanding that some kids have fast metabolisms and burn up energy faster than others takes away the blame that many larger kids feel from the culture around them. Our body size is determined by so much more than our choices around food or movement. Accepting what we cannot control (body type, shape, physical tendencies, and activity patterns we were born with) and learning about what can be influenced by habits (strength, balance, energy, acceptance) is valuable for children. We must teach this to young people, especially when even the medical establishment is so entrenched in fatphobia. I've written about this already, but it bears repeating that we need to teach children that there is no body type, shape, ability, color, gender, or sexual orientation that is better or more valuable than another. We are all just blessedly unique.

When kids and adults have a flexible, accepting relationship with their bodies, they can gracefully ride the changes of growth spurts, puberty, pregnancy, childbirth, and aging. They celebrate the fantastic, capable bodies they have. They see stretch marks and scars as signs of living, and they roll with the inevitable aging process. Yes, this is not easy to do in this selfie-oriented, image-driven culture. Start encouraging your children's resilience in the face of body change by normalizing changes and celebrating what bodies do for us.

If you have a child with a disability who is not as capable of particular activities as peers, highlight the capabilities and other essential aspects of the self. Again, all bodies and whole people are beautiful, talented, unique, and worthy. Sadly, kids and teens often hear the message that their shape and capability are worth working on more than their happiness and vitality.

Let's define some terms to consider. **Body image** is "the picture we have in our minds of the size, shape, and form of our bodies, and our feelings concerning these characteristics." Body image consists of thoughts, feelings, and attitudes related to the physical aspects of the body. Researcher Tracy Tylka has eloquently defined healthy body image as "favorable opinions of the body separate from actual appearance; acceptance of the body despite weight, shape, and imperfections; respect for the body by attending to its needs and engaging in healthy behaviors; and protection of the body by rejecting unrealistic media images." While having a healthy body image sounds great, it's still an evaluative term, so I have recently found more conflict within me about this term.

Embodiment, however, is a person's experience of living as a body. Researcher Niva Piran says, "Unlike body image, embodiment is the experience of the body as it is engaged in the world; it is a person's experience of living as a body. Embodiment is not only the individual and inner experience, but also the way the experience of the lived body is shaped by social discourse, relationships, and the 'other.'" Piran and Tylka combined their research and concluded that embodiment relates to the quality of experiences on five continuous dimensions:

1. body connection and comfort, including the ability to engage in constructive self-talk

2. agency and functionality in the world, both physically and through the voice

3. attuned self-care, reflecting the self's physical, emotional, relational, aspirational, and spiritual needs

4. experience and expression of bodily desire, including appetite and sexual desire

5. resisting objectification by immersion in meaningful pursuits and resistance to inhabiting the body as an object of gaze

An embodied individual asks, "What do I want?" instead of, "How can I be wanted and desired by others?" One's experience of embodiment can be related to socio-economic status, race, gender, ethnicity, puberty, sexuality, engagement in physical activities, safety, shame, social pressures, health issues, disability, weight bias/stigma, and internalized oppression. When I work with a client using the Somatic Experiencing™ (SE) framework, I highlight the body's "felt sense," looking at living in the body from the inside out rather than the outside in.

When we are located inside our bodies, we feel the breeze on our skin and the cool water refreshing us because we are not preoccupied with our outside image in our bathing suit. We are more in touch with our feelings and needs because we are connected to sensations within the body and make them more important than the "shoulds" we hear about behaviors with food, movement, and other activities. We are more likely to rest when we need to relax and not injure or exhaust ourselves from overexertion. We are more likely to eat when we are hungry and to eat what would be best for our bodies because we are attuned to our needs and preferences. We are more likely to respond how we want to respond when we slow down enough to notice that our nervous system is responding in a certain way. We take care of our nervous system in that awareness. **Embodiment is an experience of being at home in the body.** Some of my clients like when I use the term "body sense" instead of "body image," as it encompasses a deeper layer of the recovery work.

As parents and caregivers, we want to encourage children to listen to and not overrule the sensations of their bodies. Also, as I've said before, we must continually tell our children that they are so much more than their bodies; our bodies are just one part of ourselves (and not the most critical part). Even if you don't consider yourself a spiritual person, your children will benefit from hearing that their hearts, souls, personal qualities, inner experience, and behaviors speak so much more about who they are as people than their bodies and appearance. Yes, it's fun to dress in a way that suits your personality, but the personality matters more than the dress.

It's important to encourage kids to choose role models for qualities they admire and to notice the things deep inside themselves (and their role models) that make them feel good. Teach your children that people become unhappy when trying to be something they are not. When kids are aware and appreciate the many parts that make them who they are, they are better equipped to resist comparisons to external and idealized images. Kids will be less vulnerable to being "sold" unhealthy messages if they feel good about themselves and their unique qualities. Kids are more likely to stay true to their authentic selves, even in the face of peer and cultural pressures, if they feel good about who they are at their core.

Parents and caregivers can do a lot to promote self-confidence and self-love by highlighting those deeper, core qualities that make their children unique and not focusing on society's standards of beauty or "normalcy" as essential. As I said in Step 2, if you view your child as a whole, interesting person, they are more likely to feel that way, too.

I love being a proud mama and telling the story of my daughter in sixth grade. One day, she told me about a group of boys in her class who were judging the girls on their appearance. She and her twin sister were in the top three, but she did not like it. To my amazement and delight, she told me she marched up to one of the boys and told him to stop this practice. She said, "It makes the girls at the bottom of the list feel bad, and it makes me feel bad, too." She was trying to articulate that even being told you look gorgeous can feel objectifying and wrong. I assured her she was much more than a pretty face, and she agreed. I admired her courage and know I certainly wouldn't have been so brave in middle school.

When you focus on yourself as a complete, whole person and care for your body and self, you encourage your kids to do that, too. You give them armor against all of the judgment and comparison that is part of the pre-teen and teen years. Model self-esteem and self-confidence for your children—and share this chapter with other adults who spend time around your children, too. **Instead of telling your kids that they look cute, handsome, or pretty, tell them you are so happy to see them.** Ask them about what they are doing. Hug them and help them feel good in their bodies. Play with them and engage your bodies together. Instead of only "You look so pretty" on prom night, how about adding, "I love seeing you so radiantly happy."

My daughter Ava went through her first high school break-up and was wearing a heart necklace. I thought it was the one her recent ex-boyfriend had given her, and I asked her if she was still wearing it for a reason. She shared that it wasn't the necklace he gave her; it said, "Just Me," and she bought it herself. I just loved that. This young woman would not let her sadness about a relationship ending change the love she felt for herself. She would probably agree that she didn't always feel that solid self-love, particularly as a teen, but she had a little reminder not to lose it. I was proud of how she chose to cope with her recent challenge.

In my studies around developmental trauma, I learned that research animals would choose a soft cloth mother doll versus food on a stiff wire doll. As living beings, we need the responsiveness of others more than we need food. (Yes, some-times food can be a stand-in for attention we are not receiving because it is so connected to care and love from day one.) **Our children need responsiveness, engagement, and accessibility to the adults who love them. They need to feel they have an impact on others. The most fantastic thing is that they don't even need a whole lot of attention.** Studies and experts in child development recommend that parents be responsive, but they aren't talking about helicopter parenting. In fact, when parents are overresponsive, the child doesn't tend to develop a sense of control or agency in the world and may become overly dependent on others. Excessive parental involvement may even be associated with risk for anxiety disorders later in life.

Researchers have shown that parents don't need to get it right all the time, either. (To this, I say, "Phew, thank Goddess.") Kids do need to feel that their parents are trying. Baby cries. Does he need a diaper, or a walk, or is he cold? The trying is the important part. The baby learns, through trial and error, that he is going to get his needs met. He begins to understand that his needs matter enough to his caregivers to respond to his crying. This attunement is felt deep within the nervous system and sets up lifelong patterns toward acceptance of one's needs and desires. Peter Levine, the founder of Somatic Experiencing (SE), says, "Developmental trauma is shock trauma." It is shocking to the infant's nervous system to not have its needs responded to, impeding growth and integration.

Bonnie Badenoch, in *The Heart of Trauma: Healing the Embodied Brain in the Context of Relationships*, defines devel-opmental trauma as "any experience of fear and/or pain that doesn't have the support it needs to be digested and integrated into the flow of our developing brains." This kind of trauma can be passed down from generation to generation and heals when integration and support happen, typically in the context of supportive healing relationships. Does it shock our children's nervous systems to yell at them? Yes, but apologizing, repairing, and committing to not harming in the future can provide integration and healing. Sometimes the healing comes from caregivers, trusted others, or healing therapists.

Adverse childhood experiences (ACEs) are part of many lives. An ACE score is a tally of different types of abuse, neglect, and other hallmarks of a tough childhood. According to the Adverse Childhood Experiences study, the rougher your childhood, the higher your score is likely to be, and the higher your risk for later health problems. ACEs have been linked to various adult conditions, including increased headaches, depression, and heart disease. ACEs are believed to affect the long-term response to stress. Of course, genetic or other health habits influence physical and mental health. One's ACE score also doesn't include the positive experiences in early life that can help build resilience and protect a child from the effects of trauma. Psychologists say that having a parent or grandparent who shows love, a teacher who understands and believes in you, or a trusted friend you can confide in may alleviate the long-term effects of early trauma.

Divorce can be a traumatic experience, as can being in a family with conflict and fear. Physical and verbal abuse can be passed down from generation to generation as "the way our family operates," but this doesn't mean that harm is not done to a young, vulnerable nervous system. Children and teens are less likely to harm their bodies and themselves via disordered eating, physical self-harm, and suicidal gestures when they have validating, loving forces to counteract the traumatic ones. Families who are responsive, accessible, and engaged are protective and healing forces when children have experienced trauma in their young lives.

The Circle of Security is a fantastic parenting program (see the references at the end of this chapter) that supports parents' self-reflection on how they were parented to encourage the disruption of the transmission of harmful intergenerational trauma and the insecure attachment that can result from it. **Attachment** is measured by the typical anxiety and avoidance one feels and experiences in a relationship. One's attachment style is carried throughout life, though not set in stone, and impacts the development of adult relationships. The balm for early trauma and insecure attachment is a secure attachment to someone—even to a pet or nature. It's typically slow, deliberate work. Even if your child or a child you know has experienced early trauma, healing is possible through developing secure and trusting relationships.

Children and teens of all shapes, sizes, races, ages, abilities, sexual orientations, and gender expressions want to be seen, heard, and feel that they belong. We live in a world that often doesn't recognize, appreciate, and honor the challenges of people who are different from the mainstream. My current clinical nutrition-therapy practice in the Boston area has a considerable percentage of people in it who have found the road to expressing their sexuality or gender to be bumpy.

Many individuals use food for grounding, soothing, denial of appetite, or a sense of control when struggling with gender expression or sexual orientation that is not the majority in their families and communities.

Being open to our teens' developing diverse gender and sexual expression is essential and creates safety. Sadly, many children experience the narrow guidelines that our society deems acceptable or desirable. They often feel driven to alter their appearances, opinions, values, or preferences to feel they belong. In doing so, they lose their authentic and truest selves. Sometimes I see clients who feel they don't have any sense of self. We all have unique selves, but we sometimes lose the capacity to feel this, often because of traumatic experiences or messages from the culture that invalidate or compete with the truest sense of self.

Loss of self is at the core of an eating disorder (as well as other mental-health challenges), as the body and behaviors become a battleground—often for working through difficulties related to growing up and becoming an adult in a world that is often not inclusive, safe, or kind. Families and friends can help a lot when they model and express acceptance of all types of people. It's bumpy enough to discover that your sexual preference, gender expression, or body type does not match your peers', but it can be highly rocky if there is no place to go to talk about these experiences. Openness and inclusivity will help profoundly. Examining our biases as those who may be in the majority, learning and reading about the experiences of those who are different, and creating a judgment-free zone in our homes and communities is a fabulous starting point.

If your child or teen shows signs of a problematic relationship with food, body, or self, reach out by expressing concern and love. Remember that not all problems with eating look a certain way or necessarily change one's outward appearance. I tell parents and teachers to look for signs that kids are eating far less—or more—than they usually do, ruminating or obsessing about food or exercise, or being secretive or anxious about eating. Talking negatively about hiding, or checking one's body repeatedly in the mirror could be signs of challenges around the body. And while many kids and teens go through changes in mood and stress level, it's worth investigating significant changes that have you wondering about depression, anxiety, or obsessive-compulsive tendencies that can underlie disordered eating. Everything I just described may be part of typical adolescence, but trust your own judgment—or any other caring adult who seems concerned—when the degree of behavior or mood change seems significant.

Tell your child or teen that you are concerned because you love them. Don't comment on what they are eating or not eating—or make the focus on appearance. You would like him/her/them to get some support and help so that they can *feel better about themselves.* I recommend getting assistance for problems early and being discerning about that help. Enlist professionals (psychotherapists, registered dietitians, and medical-care providers) with expertise in eating disorders, even if your child is not yet there. If your child is younger than 12, the work will likely be with the parents only.

Just any registered dietitian or psychotherapist may not be able to address your child's concerns holistically. I have heard many stories of professionals exacerbating the problem—including nutrition professionals—particularly if they have biases against larger bodies and haven't examined them or don't have training working with eating disorders. I also encourage you to check out some parenting-oriented resources at this chapter's end.

In summary, spotlight embodiment and whole-self orientation for children by doing these things:

- Work to stop seeing your child or teen as a body. Work to see him/her/them as a whole person. When you notice that you are doing that—even complimenting your child's body or appearance too much—be kind to yourself (we're all taught to do this by our culture) and say something else. Instead of, "You look great in that dress. It's so flattering!" say, "You must be so excited for this special evening, and I can see that you will shine. I love to see you smiling." Appreciate the inner beauty and soul of your child. Practice this often. It may take lots of practice.

- When you notice your child or teen engaging in many behaviors related to their outward appearance (and teens will naturally do this), please encourage them to notice sensations, too. For example, the feel of the water on their skin or the sun's warmth on their face is an antidote to fussing about one's outward appearance. The more you do this yourself, the more you get comfortable sharing this experience with your children.

- Build a community of support around your family. Make sure your children and teens have plenty of loving, affirming adults around them, and share with them how they can show support and love for the whole-person selves of these young people. Adult role models other than parents are essential.

- If you notice a problem with food, mood, or body image, reach out. Express care and concern. Seek help from providers who specialize in disordered eating. Be discerning about the providers you choose, and ensure they are versed in Health-at-Every-Size (HAES)™ to reduce body shame.

Research suggests that early help for disordered eating creates better recovery outcomes, less relapse, and a greater likelihood that your child will grow up to have a healthy relationship with food, body, and self. This is encouraging. I see many adolescents and adults struggle and overcome these battles. They lead productive, joyful lives and often advocate for a more diverse and size-inclusive culture. They feel a sense of meaning in their lives and appreciate the miracles of their bodies and whole selves, applying that appreciation to improve their relationships with others.

Fellow parents and caregivers, I invite you to intentionally create a climate of love, support, and acceptance at home. Unfortunately, we can't do anything about many cultural and other influences on our children, but we can be a positive nurturing force amid it all. Responsiveness and acceptance, sprinkled often and with authenticity, will encourage the young people in your care to honor their minds, bodies, and whole selves—and the whole selves of those they come into connection with.

Parenting and caring for young people are not for the faint of heart. Kids bring us to our knees and hold up many challenging mirrors. Our job as caregivers is not to be perfect (who wants to live up to that?) but to strive to communicate love, care, and acceptance. In doing so, we contribute to helping the next generation love and care for themselves, others, and our wider world. What nobler task is there while we have such a short time here on this planet?

Step 10: References and Resources

Taylor, S.R. *The Body Is Not an Apology: The Power of Radical Self-Love*. Oakland, CA: Berrett-Koehler Publishers, Inc., 2018.

Hudson JL and Dodd HF. "Informing Early Intervention: preschool predictors of anxiety disorders in middle childhood." PLOS ONE. 2012; https://doi.org/10.1371/journal.pone.0042359

Tylka, T.L. "Positive psychology perspective on body image." In T.F. Cash & L. Smolak (Eds.) *Body Image: A Handbook of Science, Practice, and Prevention*. New York, NY: The Guilford Press, 2011.

Piran, N. "Embodied possibilities and disruptions: the emergence of the experience of embodiment construct from qualitative studies with girls and women." *Body Image.* 2016;18:43–60.

Tylka, T.L. and Piran N. (Eds.) *Handbook of Positive Body Image and Embodiment.* New York, NY: Oxford University Press, 2019.

Cook-Cottone, C. *Embodiment and the Treatment of Eating Disorders: The Body as a Resource in Recovery.* New York, NY: W.W. Norton, 2020.

Kite, L. and Kite, L. *More Than a Body: Your Body Is an Instrument, Not an Ornament.* New York, NY: Houghton Mifflin Harcourt Publishing, 2021.

Badenoch, B. *The Heart of Trauma: Healing the Embodied Brain in the Context of Relationships.* New York, NY: W.W. Norton, 2018.

Fay, Deirdre. *Becoming Safely Embodied: A Guide to Organize Your Mind, Body, and Heart to Feel Secure in the World.* New York, NY: Morgan James Publishing, 2021.

The Circle of Security International. https://www.circleo fsecurityinternational.com/

The Full Bloom Project: Podcast and Body Positive Parenting Guide. https://www.fullbloomproject.com/training/abc-guide

Schauster, H. *Nourish: How to Heal Your Relationship with Food, Body, and Self.* Somerville, MA: Hummingbird Press, 2018.

Crosbie, C. and Sterling, W. *How to Nourish Your Child Through an Eating Disorder: A Simple, Plate-by-Plate Approach to Rebuilding a Healthy Relationship with Food.* New York, NY: The Experiment Publishing, 2018.

Neff, K. *Self-Compassion: The Proven Power of Being Kind to Yourself.* New York, NY: Harper Collins Publishers, 2011.

Acknowledgments

I feel so much gratitude and love for the extraordinary village that helped me raise this book.

To my clients and clinical supervisees, many who allowed me to share their stories. Witnessing your hard work and dedication to healing and connecting to your whole selves is a tremendous honor.

To my numerous insightful teachers and mentors, including and especially Lisa Pearl, Linda Gelda, Wyoma, and Tricia Axom O'Brien.

Thank you to the friends and colleagues who support and inspire my creative expression. There are so many of you without whom I could not do quality work in this field, and I appreciate every one of you. Here I'll name those who were able to take the time to review all or part of this manuscript and provide valuable feedback: Beth Mayer, Lauren Manasse, Sarah McAllister, Jamie Earnhardt, Melissa David, Hannah Saxe, Sara Hart, Lisa Pearl, Amy Cantor, Anna Sweeney, Liz Fayram, and Clare Ellis.

A special thank you to Julianna DeBonis for her tireless attention to detail as my research intern. She found the references to back up the things I knew to be true but needed the evidence for. Julianna helped me with my least favorite place to spend time, social media, which is essential in order to help bring this book to those who will benefit from it.

To all the wise people whose words and research were quoted and sourced in these pages. You give this work credibility and community. I couldn't have written this book without you and your supportive contributions.

To Michele DeFilippo and Ronda Rawlins of 1106 Design for their partnership in birthing this book in a way that is consistent with my vision and values.

To the Encore Dance Ensemble for encouraging my movement and choreographic wanderings, providing balance and creative compost for my writing.

To my big crazy family, especially Mom, Dad, Joe, Amy, Emily, Peter, June, and John. Your continued steady presence and loving support are both incredible and sustaining.

In loving memory of tea parties with Nana Gloria.

To Pasha for making life full of rhythm, adventure, and love—resourcing me so that I have the spaciousness and energy to reflect, create, and write about my passions.

To Ava and Kyla, to whom this book is dedicated, for being honest, accepting, generous, and incredibly flexible. You have always made me smile, cry-laugh, and occasionally panic. You continue to be my spiritual teachers. May you flourish even more into your truest selves as you move into your adult lives.

About the Author

Heidi Schauster, MS, RD, CEDS-S, SEP is a nutrition therapist and Somatic Experiencing (SE) Practitioner in the Greater Boston area who has specialized in eating and body-image concerns for nearly 30 years. She provides individual and group counseling and clinical supervision/consultation and is particularly interested in the intersection between food and body concerns with trauma. Heidi considers herself a whole-self-wellness practitioner and Embodiment Warrior. She is the author of the award-winning book *Nourish: How to Heal Your Relationship with Food, Body, and Self* and writes the Nourishing Words newsletter on Substack. Heidi lives in Arlington, Massachusetts, with her partner and twin daughters when they aren't in college. She recently choreographed a modern dance piece about the "empty nest" performed by an ensemble of women age 40+. Heidi and her family enjoy most food that is lovingly prepared, especially if it's followed by a dishwashing dance party.

https://anourishingword.com

CONTACT

http://anourishingword.com

@NourishingWords

https://substack.com/@nourishingwords

If you liked this book:

1. I invite you to join my mailing list by adding your name and email address on my website: https://anourishing-word.com. You will receive nourishing words season-ally as well as information about in-person and online support related to the Steps outlined here. If you like reading newsletters on Substack, you will receive nourish-ing words at https://substack.com/@nourishingwords.

2. Please review the book on Amazon, Goodreads, and any other places where you review books. It takes only a couple of minutes, but it helps get this book into the hands of others who might benefit from the work.

Thank you so much!